Vocabulary Workshop
Introductory Course

- **Words in Context**
- **Analogies**
- **Multiple Meanings**
- **Synonyms, Antonyms**
- **Prefixes, Suffixes, Roots**
- **Word Origins**

HOLT, RINEHART AND WINSTON

A Harcourt Classroom Education Company

Austin • New York • Orlando • Atlanta • San Francisco • Boston • Dallas • Toronto • London

EDITORIAL

Director
Mescal Evler

Manager of Editorial Operations
Bill Wahlgren

Executive Editor
Emily G. Shenk

Project Editor
Cheryl L. Christian

Writing and Editing: Janis D. Russell

Editorial Assistant: Kim Soriano

Copyediting: Michael Neibergall, *Copyediting Manager;* Mary Malone, *Senior Copyeditor;* Joel Bourgeois, Elizabeth Dickson, Gabrielle Field, Julie A. Hill, Jane Kominek, Millicent Ondras, Theresa Reding, Dennis Scharnberg, Kathleen Scheiner, Laurie Schlesinger, *Copyeditors*

Project Administration: Marie Price, *Managing Editor;* Lori De La Garza, *Editorial Operations Coordinator;* Thomas Browne, Heather Cheyne, Diane Hardin, Mark Holland, Marcus Johnson, Jill O'Neal, Joyce Rector, Janet Riley, Kelly Tankersley, *Project Administration;* Gail Coupland, Ruth Hooker, Margaret Sanchez, *Word Processing*

Editorial Permissions: Janet Harrington, *Permissions Editor*

ART, DESIGN AND PHOTO

Graphic Services
Kristen Darby, *Manager*

Image Acquisitions: Joe London, *Director;* Tim Taylor, *Photo Research Supervisor;* Rick Benavides, *Assistant Photo Researcher;* Elaine Tate, *Supervisor;* Erin Cone, *Art Buyer*

Cover Design
Sunday Patterson

PRODUCTION

Belinda Barbosa Lopez, *Senior Production Coordinator;* Simira Davis, *Supervisor;* Nancy Hargis, *Media Production Supervisor;* Joan Lindsay, *Production Coordinator;* Beth Prevelige, *Prepress Manager*

ELECTRONIC PUBLISHING

Carol Martin, *Senior Electronic Publishing Manager;* Robert Franklin, *Electronic Publishing Manager;* Indira Konanur, *Project Coordinator;* JoAnn Brown, Richard Chavez, Jim Gaile, Heather Jernt, Lana Kaupp, Christopher Lucas, Robin McKinney, Nanda Patel, *EP staff;* Emilie Keturakis, Katelijne Lefevere, Sally Williams, *Quality Control Coordinators*

MANUFACTURING

Michael Roche, *Supervisor of Inventory and Manufacturing*

Printed in the United States of America

ISBN 0-03-056023-3

5   095   04   03   02

Consultant

Norbert Elliot, the general editor of *Vocabulary Workshop*, has a Ph.D. in English from The University of Tennessee. He is a professor of English at New Jersey Institute of Technology. A former site director for the National Writing Project, he has directed summer language arts institutes for kindergarten through twelfth-grade teachers in the public schools. A specialist in test development and evaluation of writing, Norbert Elliot has written books and articles on writing assessment, communication, and critical thinking. Dr. Elliot is the father of five children and is married to Lorna Jean Elliot, under whose care, he says, "everything thrives."

CONTENTS

The Natural World

MAKING NEW WORDS YOUR OWN 1

SKILLS AND STRATEGIES
- Context Clues
- Word Structure
- Sound Clues
- Dictionary Definitions
- Like and Opposite Meanings

CONTEXT: Amazing Nature

CONTEXT: People and Places

CONTEXT: Ecology and Environment

UNDERSTANDING NEW WORDS AND THEIR USES

SKILLS AND STRATEGIES
- Multimeaning
- Word Analysis
  Prefixes
  Suffixes
  Word Origins

CONTEXT: Amazing Nature

CONTEXT: People and Places

CONTEXT: Ecology and Environment

CONNECTING NEW WORDS AND PATTERNS

SKILLS AND STRATEGIES
- Understanding Analogies
- Types of Analogies
- Solving Analogies

READING NEW WORDS IN CONTEXT

SKILLS AND STRATEGIES
- Reading Longer Passages
- Reading Strategically

CONTEXT: Amazing Nature

CONTEXT: People and Places

CONTEXT: Ecology and Environment

The following tables list some common roots, prefixes, and suffixes. Use these tables to help you determine the meaning of a word by examining its structure.

ROOTS		
BASE	**MEANING**	**EXAMPLES**
act	to do, drive	**act**ion, **act**or, re**act**, trans**act**, en**act**
alt	high	**alt**itude, **alt**imeter
ann, enn	year	**ann**ual, per**enn**ial, bicent**enn**ial
aqua	water	**aqua**rium, **aqua**marine, **aqua**naut
aster, astro	star	**astro**nomy, **astro**nomical, **aster**isk
aud	to hear	**aud**ience, **aud**itorium, **aud**ible
biblio, bibli	book	**biblio**grapher, **biblio**mania, **bibli**cal
bio	life	**bio**logy, **bio**chemistry, **bio**degradable
cede	to go; to yield	inter**cede**, super**cede**, con**cede**
cent	one hundred	per**cent**, bicent**enn**ial, **cent**ennial
chrono	time	**chrono**logy, **chrono**meter, **chrono**scope
circ, circum	around	**circum**ference, **circ**le, **circ**ular
cred	to believe, trust	**cred**ibility, in**cred**ible, **cred**it, **cred**ential
dem	people	**dem**ocracy, **dem**agogue, epi**dem**ic
dent	tooth	**dent**ist, **dent**al, **dent**ifrice
dic, dict	to say, to speak; to assert	**dict**ion, **dict**ionary, **dict**ate
dur	hard, lasting	**dur**ation, **dur**able, en**dur**e
fin	end, limit	**fin**ish, **fin**ite, in**fin**ite, **fin**al
gen	race, family, kind	**gen**ealogy, **gen**eral, **gen**eration
geo	earth	**geo**logy, **geo**centric, **geo**dynamics
graph, gram	to write, draw, record	auto**graph**, tele**gram**, para**graph**
hab	to have, hold; to dwell	**hab**it, **hab**itat, in**hab**it
hydro	water	**hydro**gen, **hydro**dynamics, **hydro**plane
hypo	under, below	**hypo**dermic, **hypo**tension, **hypo**thermia
jur, jus, judic	law, right, judgment	**jur**ist, **jus**tify, **judic**ial
leg	law	**leg**al, **leg**islator, **leg**itimate
loc	place	**loc**al, **loc**alize, re**loc**ate, dis**loc**ate

BASE	MEANING	EXAMPLES
logue, logo	idea, word, speech, reason	dia**logue**, mono**logue**, epi**logue**, **logic**al
manu	hand	**manu**al, **manu**facture
med, medi	middle	**med**iate, **med**ieval, **med**iocre
meter, metr	measure	dia**meter**, **metr**ic, milli**meter**
morph	form	pseudo**morph**, meso**morph**, meta**morph**osis
micro	small	**micro**scope, **micro**organism
mono	one	**mono**logue, **mono**gamy, **mono**graph
mov, mob, mot	to move	**mob**, **mob**ile, re**mov**e, **mot**ion
noc, nox	night	equi**nox**, **noc**turnal, **noc**turne
ped	foot	**ped**estal, **ped**estrian, **ped**al
peri	around	**peri**meter, **peri**scope, **peri**phery
petr	rock	**petr**ify, **petr**oleum, **petr**oglyph
phon	sound, voice	**phon**etics, **phon**ics, tele**phon**e
photo	light	**photo**graphy, **photo**flash, **photo**genic
port	to carry	im**port**, ex**port**, **port**able
pyr	fire	**pyr**omania, **pyr**otechnic
sci	to know	con**sci**ence, **sci**ence, **sci**entist
scope	to see	kaleido**scope**, tele**scope**, micro**scope**
scrib, script	to write	in**scrib**e, sub**script**ion, **script**
sign	mark	**sign**al, **sign**ature, in**sign**ia
spec, spect, spic	to see, look at, behold	in**spect**, re**spect**, **spect**acle, **spec**ies
syn, sym	together	**sym**phony, **syn**thesize
techn	art, skill	**techn**ical, **techn**ology, **techn**ique
temp	time	**temp**orary, **temp**er
therm	heat	**therm**ometer, **therm**onuclear
tract	to pull, draw	at**tract**, re**tract**, **tract**ion
vis, vid	to see, look	re**vis**ion, **vid**eo, **vis**ible
volve	roll	in**volve**, re**volve**, re**volu**tion

PREFIXES		
PREFIX	**MEANING**	**EXAMPLES**
ab–	from; away from	**ab**normal, **ab**duct, **ab**sent, **ab**hor
ad–	to; motion toward; addition to	**ad**apt, **ad**dict, **ad**here, **ad**mit
aero–	air	**aero**bic, **aero**biology, **aero**space
amphi–	both, around	**amphi**bian, **amphi**theater
an–	not	**an**archy, **an**esthesia, **an**onymous
ante–	before	**ante**bellum, **ante**cede, **ante**date
anti–	against; opposite; reverse	**anti**aircraft, **anti**freeze, **anti**biotics
ap–	to; nearness to	**ap**proximate, **ap**point, **ap**proach
auto–	self	**auto**matic, **auto**graph, **auto**biography
bene–	good	**bene**diction, **bene**factor, **bene**volent
bi–	two	**bi**facial, **bi**focal, **bi**ennial
circum–	around	**circum**navigate, **circum**ference
co–, con–	together	**co**author, **co**operate, **con**front, **con**found
contra–	against	**contra**dict, **contra**distinguish, **contra**ry
de–	opposite of; away from; undo	**de**activate, **de**form, **de**grade, **de**plete, **de**scend
dis–	opposite	**dis**agree, **dis**arm, **dis**continue, **dis**honest
ex–	out; beyond; away from; former	**ex**cel, **ex**clude, **ex**hale, **ex**ile
extra–	outside; beyond; besides	**extra**ordinary, **extra**curricular
for–	not	**for**bid, **for**get, **for**go
fore–	before	**fore**cast, **fore**word, **fore**stall, **fore**thought
hyper–	more than normal; too much	**hyper**active, **hyper**critical, **hyper**tension
il–	not	**il**legal, **il**legible, **il**literate, **il**logical
im–	into	**im**mediate, **im**merse, **im**migrate, **im**port
im–	not	**im**balance, **im**mature, **im**mobilize
in–	not; go into	**in**accurate, **in**active, **in**habit
inter–	among; between	**inter**action, **inter**cede, **inter**change
intra–	within	**intra**mural, **intra**state, **intra**venous
ir–	not	**ir**redeemable, **ir**regular, **ir**responsible
mal–	wrong; bad	**mal**adjusted, **mal**function, **mal**ice
mis–	wrong; bad; no; not	**mis**fire, **mis**behave, **mis**conduct
non–	not; opposite of	**non**committal, **non**conductor, **non**partisan
ob–	against	**ob**stacle, **ob**stinate, **ob**struct, **ob**ject

PREFIXES *(continued)*		
PREFIX	**MEANING**	**EXAMPLES**
per–	through	**per**colate, **per**ceive
post–	after	**post**glacial, **post**graduate, **post**erior
pre–	before	**pre**amble, **pre**arrange, **pre**caution
pro–	before; for; in support of	**pro**gnosis, **pro**gram, **pro**logue, **pro**phet
pro–	forward	**pro**ceed, **pro**duce, **pro**ficient, **pro**gress
re–	back; again	**re**call, **re**cede, **re**flect, **re**pay
retro–	backward	**retro**active, **retro**spect, **retro**cede
se–	apart	**se**cure, **se**cede, **se**cession
self–	of the self	**self**-taught, **self**-worth, **self**-respect, **self**ish
semi–	half; partly	**semi**circle, **semi**formal, **semi**trailer
sub–	under; beneath	**sub**contract, **sub**ject, **sub**marine, **sub**merge
super–	over	**super**abound, **super**abundant, **super**human
sur–	over; above	**sur**charge, **sur**face, **sur**mount, **sur**pass
trans–	across; over	**trans**atlantic, **trans**cend, **trans**cribe, **trans**fer
ultra–	extremely	**ultra**liberal, **ultra**modern, **ultra**sonic
un–	not	**un**able, **un**comfortable, **un**certain, **un**happy

SUFFIXES		
SUFFIX	**MEANING**	**EXAMPLES**
–able, ible	able to be; capable of being	intelligible, probable, inevitable
–ade	action or process	blockade, escapade, parade
–age	action or process	marriage, pilgrimage, voyage
–al, –ial	of; like; relating to; suitable for	potential, musical, national
–ance	act; process; quality; state of being	tolerance, alliance, acceptance
–ant	one who	assistant, immigrant, merchant
–ary	of; like; relating to	customary, honorary, obituary
–ate	characteristic of; to become	officiate, consecrate, activate
–cle, –icle	small	corpuscle, cubicle, particle
–cy	fact or state of being	diplomacy, privacy, relevancy
–dom	state or quality of	boredom, freedom, martyrdom
–ence	act or state of being	occurrence, conference
–ent	doing; having; showing	fraudulent, dependent, negligent
–er	one who; that which	boxer, rancher, employer
–ery	place for; act, practice of	surgery, robbery, nursery
–esque	like	picturesque, statuesque
–ess	female	goddess, heiress, princess
–ful	full of	careful, fearful, joyful, thoughtful
–ible	capable of being	collectible, legible, divisible
–ic	relating to; characteristic of	comic, historic, poetic, public
–ify	to make; to cause to be	modify, glorify, beautify, pacify
–ion	act, condition, or result of	calculation, action, confederation
–ish	of or belonging to; characterized by	tallish, amateurish, selfish
–ism	act, practice, or result of; example	barbarism, heroism, cyncism
–ity	condition; state of being	integrity, sincerity, calamity, purity
–ive	of; relating to; belonging to; tending to	inquisitive, active, creative
–ize	make; cause to be; subject to	jeopardize, standardize, computerize
–less	without	ageless, careless, thoughtless, tireless
–let	small	islet, leaflet, owlet, rivulet, starlet
–like	like; characteristic of	childlike, waiflike
–logy	study or theory of	biology, ecology, geology

SUFFIXES *(continued)*		
SUFFIX	**MEANING**	**EXAMPLES**
–ly	every	daily, weekly, monthly, yearly
–ly	like; characteristic of	fatherly, queenly, deadly
–ly	resembling	officially, sincerely, kindly
–ment	action or process	development, government
–ment	state or quality of	amusement, amazement, predicament
–ment	product or thing	fragment, instrument, ornament
–ness	state or quality of being	kindness, abruptness, happiness
–or	one who	actor, auditor, doctor, donor
–ous	having; full of; characterized by	riotous, courageous, advantageous
–ship	state or quality of being	censorship, ownership, governorship
–some	like; tending to be	meddlesome, bothersome, noisome
–tude	state or quality of being	solitude, multitude, aptitude
–y	characterized by	thrifty, jealousy, frequency, sticky

CONTEXT

The words, phrases, or sentences around an unfamiliar word often provide clues about the word's meaning. In some cases, *signal words* can act as clues. See pp. 173–174 for further discussion of context clues.

Restatement Clues

Look for words and phrases that define an unfamiliar word or restate its meaning in familiar terms.

EXAMPLE The dried rose was as *fragile* as a butterfly's wing. **In other words,** its delicate petals can be damaged easily.

From the context, readers can tell that *fragile* means "damaged easily." The phrase *in other words* signals that the words *easily damaged* restate the meaning of the word *fragile*.

Restatement Signal Words		
in other words	that is	these

Example Clues

Examples sometimes give us hints to a word's meaning. If an unfamiliar word means a certain type of thing, action, or characteristic, examples of the type can be excellent clues to the word's meaning.

EXAMPLE When our neighbors travel, they always look for comfortable *accommodations,* **such as** a beach cottage, hotel suite, or mountain cabin.

From the context, readers can tell that the word *accommodations* means "a place to stay." The words *such as* signal that the list of places to stay provides examples of *accommodations*.

Example Signal Words		
for example	such as	in that
likewise	especially	

Contrast/Antonym Clues

Look for words or phrases that are the opposite of a word's meaning.

EXAMPLE Knowledge is a *remedy* for many environmental problems, **but** knowledge without action cannot cure the ills.

From the context, readers can tell that *remedy* means "cure." The word **but** signals that *remedy* contrasts with the phrase "cannot cure."

Contrast/Antonym Signal Words			
but	not	in contrast	on the other hand
however	still	although	some . . . but others

Keyword Clues

Look for words or phrases that modify or are related to the unfamiliar word.

EXAMPLE The two characters in my story believe it is their *destiny* to be enemies. Their elders have taught them that this is **meant to be.**

From the context, readers can tell that *destiny* means "something that necessarily happens to a person." The words *meant to be* signal the meaning of the word.

Definition/Explanation Clues

A sentence may actually define or explain an unfamiliar word.

EXAMPLE Alan will help the woman once she **escapes** and becomes a *fugitive* from her troubled country.

From the context, readers can tell that *fugitive* means "runaway." The word *escapes* signals the meaning of the word.

How We Make New Words Our Own

Use the **Context Structure Sound Dictionary (CSSD)** strategy to improve your vocabulary, to make new words your own. Use one or more of the strategies to determine the meanings of each word you do not know. The exercises that follow will show you how to go about making new words your own.

HOW TO DO EXERCISE 1 — Wordbusting

In these exercises, you will read the Vocabulary Word in a sentence. You will figure out the word's meaning by looking at its **context,** its **structure,** and its **sound.** Then you will look up the word in a **dictionary** and write its meaning *as it is used in the sentence.*

Here is an example of the Wordbusting strategy, using the word *manuscript.*

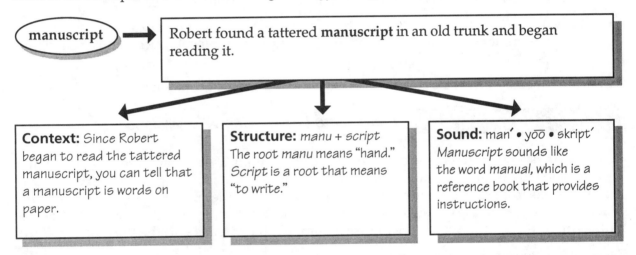

manuscript → Robert found a tattered **manuscript** in an old trunk and began reading it.

Context: Since Robert began to read the tattered manuscript, you can tell that a manuscript is words on paper.

Structure: manu + script The root *manu* means "hand." *Script* is a root that means "to write."

Sound: man' • yoo • skript' *Manuscript* sounds like the word *manual,* which is a reference book that provides instructions.

Dictionary: "a handwritten or typewritten document or paper, especially a copy of an author's work"

Hint #1 **Context:** Look for clues to the meaning of the word in the sentence. For example, "reading" is a keyword that helps reveal the meaning of *manuscript.*

Hint #2 **Structure:** Examine the word parts for roots, prefixes, and suffixes that you know. Consult the word-part tables on pages ix–xiv for meanings of parts you do not know.

Hint #3 **Sound:** Say the word aloud and listen for any word parts you know.

Hint #4 **Dictionary:** If you cannot determine a word's meaning from applying context, structure, and sound strategies, look up the unfamiliar word in a dictionary. Read all the definitions, and choose one that best fits the given sentence.

In this exercise, you will again see the new word used in a sentence. This exercise gives you the word's definition, and you must match the word in the sentence with its meaning. The word may be used in the same way as it was used in Wordbusting, or it may be used in a new way.

Here's an example of a Context Clues exercise:

COLUMN A	**COLUMN B**
_D_ **1.** word: _decrease_ *v.* to become smaller; to lessen; *n.* a lessening	(D) Recent years have seen a steady rise in the number of cat owners. On the other hand, there has been a **decrease** in the number of dog owners.

Hint #1 First, scan the definitions in Column A. Then, read Column B and look for clues to the meaning of the word. Here, the words "on the other hand" tell us that the sentence containing the word **decrease** contrasts with the sentence containing the words "a steady rise." Thus, the correct definition is probably the opposite of "a steady rise."

Hint #2 Read column A and look for a likely definition of the word. In the example, the student chose the definition that contained the meaning "a lessening," which is most nearly the opposite of "a rise."

Hint #3 Write the word in the blank so that later you can find its definition at a glance.

A synonym is a word that has practically the same meaning as another word. An antonym is a word opposite in meaning to another word. In the Like Meanings part of Exercise 3, you will be asked to find the synonym for (or, in some cases, the phrase that best defines) the Vocabulary Word. In the Opposite Meanings part of Exercise 3, you will be asked to find the antonym for (or, in some cases, the phrase that means the opposite of) the Vocabulary Word.

Here is an example of a Like Meanings item:

21. **decrease** the shedding of fur
   (A) remove
   (B) make comfortable
   (C) add to
   (D) lessen

Hint #1 Don't be fooled by choices that are closely related to the Vocabulary Word. Choice A may be tempting, but the removal of shedding is more extreme than a **decrease** in shedding.

Hint #2 Don't be fooled by distantly related choices. An animal may be more comfortable when it sheds, but there is no direct link between **decrease** and Choice B.

Hint #3 Don't be fooled by the opposite of the Vocabulary Word. Choice C would be the correct choice if this were an Opposite Meanings exercise, but here you are looking for a similar meaning.

MAKING NEW WORDS YOUR OWN

Lesson 1 | CONTEXT: Amazing Nature

The Humpback: A Whale of a Singer

Last winter, my family and I went on a whale watch. The small boat we were in moved slowly across the water. Suddenly, a huge humpback whale sprang from the water, curved its back, and disappeared into the waves. When it was underwater, we could hear it singing. How? The boat had an underwater microphone called a *hydrophone,* which picked up sounds from deep in the water.

In the following exercises, you will have the opportunity to expand your vocabulary by reading about humpback whales. Below are ten Vocabulary Words that will be used.

definite	descendant	majority	reliable	twilight
deny	doubtful	navigator	symbol	vivid

EXERCISE 1 | *Wordbusting* ✍

Directions. Follow these instructions for this word and the nine words on the next page.
- Figure out the word's meaning by looking at its **context,** its **structure,** and its **sound.** Fill in at least one of the three **CSS** boxes. Alternate which boxes you complete.
- Then, look up the word in a dictionary, read all of its meanings, and write the meaning of the word as it is used in the sentence.
- Follow this same process for each of the Vocabulary Words on the next page. You will need to draw your own map for each word. Use a separate sheet of paper.

1.

(definite) → | Although whale songs are still being studied, some facts are now clear: It is **definite** that only male humpbacks sing, and that all those in the same group sing the same tune. |

Context:

Structure:

Sound:

Dictionary:

2.

deny → Whale experts do not **deny** that it is still a mystery why the complicated arrangement of certain tones and sounds changes from year to year.

3.

doubtful → I had heard about whale songs, but when the guide said we would hear them, I was **doubtful**. How could that possibly happen?

4.

reliable → Yet, we felt that the people in charge of the whale watch were **reliable**. We knew we could depend on them for accurate information.

5.

navigator → The **navigator** of our boat talked to us as he directed our course to keep us within sight of the humpback. He told us that baleen whales are some of the largest animals in the world.

6.

majority → Baleen whales, including the humpback, are toothless. However, more than half—that is, the **majority**—of whale species have teeth.

7.

descendant → Humpbacks spend their summers in polar waters and their winters in warm seas, where their calves are born. As the older humpbacks die off, their **descendants** continue to return to the same areas year after year.

8.

twilight → Just after sunset, we headed back to shore. In the **twilight,** I looked at the water for one last sight of the magnificent whale we had been watching.

9.

symbol → Once, whales represented only economic gain. Now many people see the whale as a **symbol** of the need for humans to protect the oceans' environment. Whales stand for the beauty and wonder of all ocean life.

10.

vivid → Seeing and hearing the humpback is one of the most **vivid** experiences of my life. Because it is so unforgettable, I am going to do all that I can to help protect whales from extinction.

EXERCISE 2 *Context Clues* ✍

Directions. Scan the definitions in Column A. Then, think about how the boldface words are used in the sentences in Column B. To complete the exercise, match each definition in Column A with the correct Vocabulary Word from Column B. Write the letter of your choice on the line provided. Finally, write the Vocabulary Word on the line before the definition.

COLUMN A	COLUMN B
B **11.** word: Majority : *n.* more than half the total; the greater part	(A) Whales are warmblooded marine mammals. They are the **descendants** of land mammals that adapted to the sea millions of years ago.
D **12.** word: definite : *adj.* having limits; certain	(B) In polar waters each humpback eats over four thousand pounds of food a day. The **majority** of this food is tiny sea creatures.
I **13.** word: Symbol : *n.* something that stands for or represents something else	(C) I had hoped that while the sun was still up, before **twilight**, I would see a mother humpback with a calf, but none were visible.
G **14.** word: doubtful : *adj.* not clear; uncertain	(D) Laws protect whales by setting a **definite** distance the watchers must stay from the whales. The boats must not cross over the set boundary.
J **15.** word: navigator : *n.* a person who steers or directs a ship or an aircraft	(E) When people observe the humpbacks, they carry away **vivid** impressions clearly locked in their memories.
E **16.** word: vivid : *adj.* lively; bright; clearly perceived by the mind	(F) **Reliable**, or trustworthy, researchers say that whaling has reduced the numbers of whales, including the humpback, to dangerously low levels.
H **17.** word: deny : *v.* to refuse to give; to reject as untrue	(G) It is still **doubtful**, even with bans on most whaling, whether some species will survive. No one knows for sure.
C **18.** word: twilight : *n.* the period from sunset to dark; *adj.* pertaining to the period from sunset to dark	(H) When our class formed an environmental club, I didn't **deny** them the use of my articles and books about humpbacks. Now everyone in the club uses them.
A **19.** word: descendants : *n.* something that comes from an earlier form; offspring	(I) The club members voted to use the humpback as a **symbol** to represent the club's support of endangered wildlife.
F **20.** word: reliable : *adj.* dependable; trustworthy	(J) One of our members has decided to become a **navigator** and to work on a ship that tracks whales for a wildlife-protection organization.

EXERCISE 3 *Like Meanings and Opposite Meanings* ✍

Directions. For each item below, circle the letter of the choice that means the same, or about the same, as the boldface word.

21. a **vivid** ocean sunset
   (A) light
   (B) bright
   (C) dark
   (D) dull

22. the ship's **navigator**
   (A) person who steers the ship
   (B) anyone who goes on a ship
   (C) whale-watching guide
   (D) person who is lost

23. the **majority** of the whale watchers
   (A) exactly half
   (B) less than half
   (C) every one
   (D) more than half

24. the **symbol** of ocean life
   (A) reality
   (B) interest
   (C) representative
   (D) character

25. a **definite** sign
   (A) important
   (B) certain
   (C) invisible
   (D) similar

Directions. For each item below, circle the letter of the choice that means the opposite, or about the opposite, of the boldface word.

26. the **twilight** cruise
   (A) between sunset and dark
   (B) the middle of the night
   (C) between sunrise and noon
   (D) rainy season

27. **denied** bothering the whales
   (A) rejected as untrue
   (B) admitted
   (C) continued
   (D) stopped

28. the **reliable** guide
   (A) trustworthy
   (B) honest
   (C) undependable
   (D) independent

29. the **descendants** of the humpbacks
   (A) ancestors
   (B) children
   (C) cousins
   (D) region

30. to be **doubtful** that whales could sing
   (A) amazed
   (B) suspicious
   (C) undecided
   (D) certain

MAKING NEW WORDS YOUR OWN

Lesson 2 | **CONTEXT: Amazing Nature**

Fire-breathing Myths: Chinese Dragons

What do you think of when you picture a dragon? A scary, cruel monster? An enormous fire-breathing lizard with a long, scaly tail? This is how many people think of dragons. In China and much of Asia, the dragon is considered to be a friendly, even a lucky, creature. Chinese myths depict dragons being ridden by the gods. Two popular dragon festivals are still held in China. One is the dragon dance, held during the Chinese New Year celebrations. The other is the dragon boat festival, which may originally have been a rainmaking festival.

In the following exercises, you will have the opportunity to expand your vocabulary by reading about Chinese dragons. These ten Vocabulary Words will be used.

astonish	innumerable	journalism	quote	summarize
conference	interview	legend	session	unexpectedly

EXERCISE 1 *Wordbusting* ✍

Directions. Follow these instructions for this word and the nine words on the next page.
- Figure out the word's meaning by looking at its **context,** its **structure,** and its **sound.** Fill in at least one of the three **CSS** boxes. Alternate which boxes you complete.
- Then, look up the word in a dictionary, read all of its meanings, and write the meaning of the word as it is used in the sentence.
- Follow this same process for each of the Vocabulary Words on the next page. You will need to draw your own map for each word. Use a separate sheet of paper.

1.

(astonish) ⟶ Does it **astonish** you to learn that in Chinese tradition the dragon is a sign of good luck? It surprised me.

Context:	Structure:	Sound:

Dictionary:

2.

unexpectedly ➤ The Chinese also believed that angry dragons could cause a lot of trouble **unexpectedly**. For instance, a flood or storm that occurred suddenly without warning might be caused by a dragon.

3.

conference ➤ In some of the dragon myths, rulers would hold **conferences**. At these meetings, they would discuss how they could honor the dragons.

4.

session ➤ In the story "Liu Yi and the Dragon King," Liu meets with the dragon king. In this **session,** they discuss the king's daughter.

5.

summarize ➤ I will briefly **summarize** the story of "The Dragon's Pearl." First, a young boy finds a pearl that belongs to a dragon. The pearl makes everything—grass, money, and rice—multiply. By accident, the boy swallows the pearl and turns into a dragon.

6.

legend ➤ Have you ever heard the **legend** of the dragon of the Gaoliang Bridge? It is one of China's oldest and most popular stories.

7.

quote ➤ The storyteller **quoted** a statement made by an ancient Chinese emperor and then translated the words for us.

8.

innumerable ➤ Every year **innumerable** people—too many to count—attend the dragon dance in San Francisco.

9.

journalism ➤ Some reporters in the field of **journalism** collect and publish news about Chinese cultural events.

10.

interview ➤ They **interview** older people who remember the traditions. Sometimes they need a translator for these face-to-face conversations.

EXERCISE 2 — Context Clues

Directions. Scan the definitions in Column A. Then, think about how the boldface words are used in the sentences in Column B. To complete the exercise, match each definition in Column A with the correct Vocabulary Word from Column B. Write the letter of your choice on the line provided. Finally, write the Vocabulary Word on the line before the definition.

COLUMN A	COLUMN B

COLUMN A

_____ **11.** word: _____:
v. to amaze; to surprise

_____ **12.** word: _____:
n. a popular story or myth handed down for generations; a person whose deeds are remembered as stories; a note on an illustration or map

_____ **13.** word: _____:
n. a face-to-face meeting for evaluating or questioning; *v.* to meet with for the purpose of evaluating or asking questions

_____ **14.** word: _____:
adv. suddenly; in an unannounced way; in a way not known before

_____ **15.** word: _____:
v. to reproduce word for word; to refer to as an example; to state, as a price; *n.* words repeated exactly

_____ **16.** word: _____:
adj. too many to be counted; countless

_____ **17.** word: _____:
n. a formal meeting for discussion

_____ **18.** word: _____:
n. writing and publishing news

_____ **19.** word: _____:
n. a meeting of a group; a series of such meetings; a period of activity; a school semester or term

_____ **20.** word: _____:
v. to give a brief account of; to say briefly

COLUMN B

(A) Saint George, who is said to have fought a dragon in fourteenth-century England, has become a **legend**. His deeds are still remembered.

(B) Like the European dragon, the Chinese dragon is believed to guard **innumerable** priceless treasures. Countless items are hidden in the dragon's lair.

(C) It is difficult to **summarize** Chinese beliefs about dragons. There are just too many to describe in a few words.

(D) In an **interview,** the Chinese storyteller Li Cho discussed Chinese dragons. This face-to-face discussion was videotaped.

(E) To **quote** a famous Chinese emperor, "The dragon is the symbol of the throne."

(F) **Journalism** cannot capture the excitement of the dragon-boat race. Reading the news is just not the same as being there!

(G) The colorful costumes worn during the dragon-boat festival will **astonish** you and take your breath away.

(H) Storytelling **sessions** in China have always been popular group activities.

(I) Dragon stories were the main topic at a recent **conference** of folklore experts.

(J) Just when we thought he was finished, our teacher **unexpectedly** added a dragon myth to the list of readings for tomorrow.

EXERCISE 3 *Like Meanings and Opposite Meanings* 👈

Directions. For each item below, circle the letter of the choice that means the same, or about the same, as the boldface word.

21. to **astonish** with a roar
   (A) respond
   (B) surprise
   (C) call to
   (D) yell at

22. an **interview** with a king
   (A) meeting
   (B) audition
   (C) dance
   (D) argument

23. **journalism** in San Francisco
   (A) storytelling
   (B) celebration
   (C) myth-making
   (D) news-writing

24. to **quote** the price of
   (A) state
   (B) misunderstand
   (C) pay
   (D) hear

25. an afternoon **session**
   (A) nap
   (B) meal
   (C) meeting
   (D) fight

Directions. For each item below, circle the letter of the choice that means the opposite, or about the opposite, of the boldface word.

26. a **conference** in July
   (A) family dinner
   (B) competition
   (C) informal meeting
   (D) series of meetings

27. the **innumerable** scales on the dragon's back
   (A) slimy
   (B) few
   (C) hard
   (D) countless

28. a **legend** in Chinese culture
   (A) respected scholar
   (B) well-known reporter
   (C) little-known figure
   (D) mythical emperor

29. to **summarize** a dragon story
   (A) describe in full detail
   (B) predict accurately
   (C) understand fully
   (D) give a brief account of

30. dragons appearing **unexpectedly**
   (A) as predicted
   (B) in formation
   (C) angrily
   (D) at a low altitude

MAKING NEW WORDS YOUR OWN

Lesson 3 | **CONTEXT:** Amazing Nature

Earthquakes: Rocking and Rolling

Imagine that you are sitting on the couch reading a book when the ground begins to tremble. You hold your breath until the shaking stops. You have just experienced an earthquake! An earthquake occurs when pressure builds underground, often along a fault where two large pieces of rock meet. The rock shifts or breaks to relieve the pressure. Not all earthquakes can be felt above ground. Sometimes the only way scientists know there has been an earthquake is if they record it on a special machine called a *seismograph*.

In the following exercises, you will have the opportunity to expand your vocabulary by reading about earthquakes. These ten Vocabulary Words will be used.

collapse	complex	fatal	incident	predict
collide	disastrous	foundation	nuisance	rash

EXERCISE 1 *Wordbusting*

Directions. Follow these instructions for this word and the nine words on the next page.
- Figure out the word's meaning by looking at its **context,** its **structure,** and its **sound.** Fill in at least one of the three **CSS** boxes. Alternate which boxes you complete.
- Then, look up the word in a dictionary, read all of its meanings, and write the meaning of the word as it is used in the sentence.
- Follow this same process for each of the Vocabulary Words on the next page. You will need to draw your own map for each word. Use a separate sheet of paper.

1.

(collapse) ⟶ Recent efforts to make earthquake insurance available to all Californians have **collapsed.** Discussions have broken down and further talks have been canceled.

Context:	Structure:	Sound:

Dictionary:

2.

collide → Tsunamis are tidal waves caused by earthquakes. Great walls of water, sometimes two hundred feet high, **collide** with the shore at incredible speeds.

3.

complex → Before an earthquake, a **complex** series of events happens under the earth. The only sign of all this complicated activity, however, may be a slight tremor.

4.

disastrous → San Francisco has been the site of two **disastrous** earthquakes—in 1906 and 1989. Both earthquakes caused great damage.

5.

fatal → Earthquakes can be **fatal**. More than 230,000 people died in 1976 in a quake in northern China; in 1988, an earthquake killed 25,000 people in Armenia.

6.

foundation → The **foundation** of the Transamerica Pyramid in San Francisco is designed to be earthquake-proof. When the earth shakes, the base of the building rolls back and forth.

7.

incident → Sometimes earthquakes cause changes in the level of the earth's surface. A major shock hit Alaska in 1899. After this **incident,** some parts of the sea floor were fifty feet higher.

8.

nuisance → Planning ahead for earthquakes can seem like a bother. Still, in spite of the **nuisance,** it is wise to think ahead.

9.

predict → Some people believe that weather and animal behavior can help **predict** earthquakes and can warn people when the earthquakes might happen.

10.

rash → Any region that has had earthquakes in the past may expect them in the future, and people who live in these places should not be **rash**. To disregard the danger of earthquakes would be careless behavior indeed.

EXERCISE 2 *Context Clues* 🖎

Directions. Scan the definitions in Column A. Then, think about how the boldface words are used in the sentences in Column B. To complete the exercise, match the definition in Column A with the correct Vocabulary Word from Column B. Write the letter of your choice on the line provided. Finally, write the Vocabulary Word on the line before the definition.

COLUMN A	COLUMN B

COLUMN A

_____ **11.** word: _____:
adj. acting in a hasty or reckless manner;
n. spots that erupt on the skin;
a large number of instances that occur
suddenly

_____ **12.** word: _____:
n. the base on which something is built;
an establishment or fund; basis

_____ **13.** word: _____:
adj. seriously harmful; damaging

_____ **14.** word: _____:
n. something or somebody causing
annoyance or inconvenience

_____ **15.** word: _____:
v. to crash; to come together with a
violent impact; to come into conflict

_____ **16.** word: _____:
v. to foretell an event or events

_____ **17.** word: _____:
n. something that happens; an event

_____ **18.** word: _____:
v. to fall down or apart; to break down
suddenly; *n.* the act of falling down

_____ **19.** word: _____:
adj. destructive; resulting in death;
decisive; having to do with fate

_____ **20.** word: _____:
adj. complicated; difficult; *n.* a group of
related buildings; a group of feelings
that influence a person's behavior

COLUMN B

(A) After the Mexico City earthquake of 1985, a special **foundation,** or organization, was set up to help the survivors.

(B) The earth experiences about fifty thousand earthquakes each year. Luckily, however, a **disastrous** earthquake only occurs about once every two years. The others do little damage.

(C) Most quakes are light shocks. They might be a **nuisance,** but they do not cause serious harm.

(D) Computers help scientists **predict** earthquakes. However, it is still hard to know for certain where and when an earthquake will strike.

(E) An earthquake may be occurring nearby at this very moment, but it may be so slight that you are unaware of the **incident**.

(F) Earthquakes usually do not harm people directly. The injuries are caused when objects **collide** or smash into each other or when buildings fall down or catch fire.

(G) One of the earliest recorded **fatal** earthquakes took place in Corinth, Greece, in A.D. 856. About forty-five thousand people were killed.

(H) After a severe earthquake, damage can be extensive. An entire apartment **complex,** for example, can be destroyed. It is shocking to see a set of buildings become a pile of rubble.

(I) Many one- and two-story buildings survive serious earthquakes. They usually do not **collapse** unless their roofs are too heavy.

(J) After an earthquake, goods are left exposed, and, sometimes, a **rash** of burglaries occurs. This sudden increase in crime is usually temporary.

EXERCISE 3   *Like Meanings and Opposite Meanings* 👈

Directions. For each item below, circle the letter of the choice that means the same, or about the same, as the boldface word.

21. to **collide** with great force
    (A) bend
    (B) divide
    (C) rise
    (D) crash

22. a **foundation** of self-respect
    (A) basis
    (B) high expectation
    (C) definition
    (D) certain kind

23. an earthshaking **incident**
    (A) party
    (B) event
    (C) story
    (D) visit

24. an inferiority **complex**
    (A) deep wishes
    (B) interesting diagnosis
    (C) set of feelings
    (D) serious problem

25. to **predict** an earthquake
    (A) analyze
    (B) live through
    (C) describe
    (D) foretell

Directions. For each item below, circle the letter of the choice that means the opposite, or about the opposite, of the boldface word.

26. the **collapse** of homes
    (A) expansion
    (B) building
    (C) selling
    (D) painting

27. a **disastrous** tidal wave
    (A) helpful
    (B) harmful
    (C) surprising
    (D) enormous

28. a **fatal** event
    (A) important
    (B) boring
    (C) free-for-all
    (D) life-giving

29. a great **nuisance**
    (A) annoyance
    (B) explanation
    (C) belief
    (D) help

30. a **rash** decision
    (A) thoughtful
    (B) thoughtless
    (C) similar
    (D) ignorant

MAKING NEW WORDS YOUR OWN

Lesson 4 | CONTEXT: Amazing Nature
There They Go Again: Animal Migrations

Twice a year, in the spring and fall, certain animals travel hundreds and sometimes thousands of miles. These animals include birds, whales, bats, caribou, butterflies, and fish. Scientists are still trying to understand how animals find their way around the globe. Some birds, for instance, fly thousands of miles and return in the spring to the same nests they left in the fall. How do they find their way back?

In the following exercises, you will have the opportunity to expand your vocabulary by reading about animal migrations. Below are ten Vocabulary Words that will be used.

aviation	departure	disturb	instinct	miraculous
demonstration	detect	exception	locally	unfavorable

EXERCISE 1   *Wordbusting* ✍

Directions. Follow these instructions for this word and the nine words on the next page.
- Figure out the word's meaning by looking at its **context,** its **structure,** and its **sound.** Fill in at least one of the three **CSS** boxes. Alternate which boxes you complete.
- Then, look up the word in a dictionary, read all of its meanings, and write the meaning of the word as it is used in the sentence.
- Follow this same process for each of the Vocabulary Words on the next page. You will need to draw your own map for each word. Use a separate sheet of paper.

1.

aviation ⟶ The Arctic Tern is a miracle of **aviation**. It flies about twenty-two thousand miles each year—as much as some airplanes!

Context:	Structure:	Sound:

Dictionary:

2.

(demonstration) ➤ A **demonstration** was held at the university last Friday. Students wanted to show their support for blue whales, which are hunted when they migrate.

3.

(departure) ➤ The **departure** of the Pacific salmon from the rivers marks the beginning of a long journey. Four years after leaving the rivers, the salmon will return and swim upstream against a fierce current.

4.

(detect) ➤ Birds that travel at night **detect** the positions of the stars. Seeing the stars helps them travel in the right direction.

5.

(disturb) ➤ The destruction of the rain forest and other nesting places means that fewer songbirds breed each year. This problem upsets and **disturbs** many scientists.

6.

(exception) ➤ Most mammals cannot fly. The bat is an **exception**. It can fly quite well.

7.

(instinct) ➤ Animals migrate by **instinct**. Salmon, for example, use their natural sense of smell to help them return to their original stream.

8.

(locally) ➤ Whooping cranes are rare, endangered birds. **Locally** popular in Texas, where they spend the winter, they are eagerly welcomed to the area each year.

9.

(miraculous) ➤ Hummingbirds, which weigh only one eighth of an ounce, do a **miraculous** thing every year. They fly about five hundred miles across the Gulf of Mexico. Amazingly, they make the trip in about ten hours!

10.

(unfavorable) ➤ There are many reasons that animals migrate. In some cases, **unfavorable** conditions, such as a lack of food or water, cause the animals to move.

EXERCISE 2 *Context Clues*

Directions. Scan the definitions in Column A. Then, think about how the boldface words are used in the sentences in Column B. To complete the exercise, match each definition in Column A with the correct Vocabulary Word from Column B. Write the letter of your choice on the line provided. Finally, write the Vocabulary Word on the line before the definition.

COLUMN A	COLUMN B

_____ **11.** word: _____:
n. the art or science of flying airplanes

(A) Migration can be studied **locally**. Find out which creatures in your area migrate and where they go.

_____ **12.** word: _____:
v. to break up order or quiet; to upset someone emotionally; to bother

(B) After the **departure** of some animals in your area, observe whether others take their place for the season.

_____ **13.** word: _____:
adj. like a miracle; wonderful; almost beyond understanding

(C) At the nature center, the ranger held a **demonstration** to show how wildlife in our area changes with the seasons.

_____ **14.** word: _____:
adv. within a given area

(D) If you look carefully, you may **detect** bands attached to the legs of some migrating birds. These bands are placed there by scientists and are used to track the birds' movements.

_____ **15.** word: _____:
n. to behave in a way that is natural, or second nature; an aptitude or talent

(E) Researchers are still studying how birds use **instinct** when migrating. Some birds that fly by day automatically use the sun as a navigational tool.

_____ **16.** word: _____:
adj. not approved; not helpful

(F) As researchers come to understand some aspects of migration, others still seem **miraculous**. How can these animals and insects navigate so precisely?

_____ **17.** word: _____:
n. a person to whom or a case to which something does not apply; something left out

(G) When monarch butterflies migrate to and from Mexico, wind and other obstacles do not **disturb** them.

_____ **18.** word: _____:
n. the act of proving or showing something through example; an outward display of, or a gathering to express, an opinion or protest

(H) Birds that migrate at night can become confused by **unfavorable** weather conditions, such as heavy fog that lasts for a long period of time.

_____ **19.** word: _____:
v. to discover; to notice something not obvious

(I) People in **aviation** tell interesting stories. Pilots sometimes see thousands of migrating birds flying too high to be seen from the ground.

_____ **20.** word: _____:
n. the act of going away or leaving

(J) The humpback, a baleen whale, is an **exception** to many migrating animals. Unlike them, it travels to colder regions to find food.

EXERCISE 3 *Like Meanings and Opposite Meanings* ✍

Directions. For each item below, circle the letter of the choice that means the same, or about the same, as the boldface word.

21. the science of **aviation**
    (A) diving
    (B) migration
    (C) biology
    (D) flying

22. to use **instinct**
    (A) inborn ability
    (B) understanding
    (C) intelligence
    (D) another method

23. a **demonstration** of the facts
    (A) simplifying
    (B) fight
    (C) showing
    (D) division

24. to **detect** migrating whales
    (A) hunt
    (B) follow
    (C) assist
    (D) discover

25. an **exception,** the flying bat
    (A) migrating mammal
    (B) special case
    (C) warmblooded mammal
    (D) specific example

Directions. For each item below, circle the letter of the choice that means the opposite, or about the opposite, of the boldface word.

26. an **unfavorable** climate
    (A) natural
    (B) agreeable
    (C) unhealthy
    (D) rainy

27. the **departure** of the caribou
    (A) arrival
    (B) death
    (C) absence
    (D) leaving

28. to **disturb** a gathering of birds
    (A) restore calm to
    (B) openly observe
    (C) greatly annoy
    (D) track down

29. birds nesting **locally**
    (A) nearby
    (B) along the coast
    (C) within an area
    (D) far away

30. a **miraculous** event
    (A) unhealthy
    (B) amazing
    (C) ordinary
    (D) wonderful

MAKING NEW WORDS YOUR OWN

Lesson 5 CONTEXT: Amazing Nature

Lava Alert at Hawaii's Kilauea Volcano

Kilauea is one of the most active volcanoes in the world. It lies on the eastern slopes of the Mauna Loa volcano in Hawaii Volcanoes National Park. The park is located on the big island of Hawaii. Kilauea's crater is two and a half miles long, two miles wide, and four hundred feet deep. At one point, a smaller crater within this large one held a lake of molten lava. Kilauea erupts regularly, and visitors to the park often see these eruptions.

In the following exercises, you will have the opportunity to expand your vocabulary by reading about Hawaii's Kilauea volcano. These ten Vocabulary Words will be used.

| caution | dread | generation | heroic | previous |
| congratulate | error | gratitude | involve | separation |

EXERCISE 1 Wordbusting ✍

Directions. Follow these instructions for this word and the nine words on the next page.
- Figure out the word's meaning by looking at its **context,** its **structure,** and its **sound.** Fill in at least one of the three **CSS** boxes. Alternate which boxes you complete.
- Then, look up the word in a dictionary, read all of its meanings, and write the meaning of the word as it is used in the sentence.
- Follow this same process for each of the Vocabulary Words on the next page. You will need to draw your own map for each word. Use a separate sheet of paper.

1.

(caution) → Backpackers enjoy the eighteen-mile Mauna Loa Trail. They must be aware that the high altitude makes breathing more difficult and use **caution**.

Context:

Structure:

Sound:

Dictionary:

2.
(generation) ➔ Devastation Trail leads through a forest that was burned by cinder and lava in 1959. An entire **generation** of trees, all from the same time period, were killed.

3.
(separation) ➔ **Separation** on the trails is something that all hikers on Kilauea should avoid. It is important for hikers to stay together.

4.
(gratitude) ➔ We thanked the park ranger for showing us the Thurston Lava Tube. We walked through the tube, which is more than 450 feet long, and we felt **gratitude** for the special experience.

5.
(heroic) ➔ The Hawaiians believed that the goddess Pele lived in the steaming crater. They thought that anyone brave enough to walk near the crater was truly **heroic**!

6.
(congratulate) ➔ Anyone spending a day on the trails should be **congratulated,** or praised, for their efforts.

7.
(dread) ➔ Some visitors to Kilauea feel **dread**. They are afraid the volcano might erupt and harm them.

8.
(previous) ➔ From 1823 to 1924, this crater was full of bubbling molten lava. **Previous** visitors had a thrill that today's tourists can only imagine.

9.
(error) ➔ It would be an **error** to say that no one has been injured by Kilauea. In 1924, a photographer was killed by a falling rock from the crater.

10.
(involve) ➔ A visit to the Volcano House, a famous hotel on the rim of the crater, can **involve** many activities. A typical visit, for example, may include watching a film of an eruption.

EXERCISE 2 Context Clues ✍

Directions. Scan the definitions in Column A. Then, think about how the boldface words are used in the sentences in Column B. To complete the exercise, match each definition in Column A with the correct Vocabulary Word from Column B. Write the letter of your choice on the line provided. Finally, write the Vocabulary Word on the line before the definition.

COLUMN A	COLUMN B
_____ **11.** word: _____: *n.* a feeling of grateful appreciation for something received or something done	(A) Our **previous** visit to Kilauea was not as interesting as the trip this time.
_____ **12.** word: _____: *n.* a warning; carefulness; *v.* to warn	(B) Some fearful people **dread** walking into the Kilauea Iki crater. Although it is cool today, twenty-five years ago it was a boiling—and frightening—lake of lava.
_____ **13.** word: _____: *v.* to include; to relate to; to make busy; to make complicated	(C) A **heroic** Hawaiian queen once walked right up to the edge of the crater while Kilauea was erupting.
_____ **14.** word: _____: *n.* a wrong belief or opinion; a wrongdoing; a mistake	(D) To believe that Kilauea will stop erupting is an **error**. Scientists can tell you correctly that Kilauea is still active.
_____ **15.** word: _____: *v.* to express pleasure for general good fortune or success	(E) I **caution** all visitors to Kilauea to avoid wandering off the trails. I warn them that it is easy and very dangerous to get lost!
_____ **16.** word: _____: *adj.* brave; strong and noble; like a hero	(F) I **congratulate** and applaud you for backpacking to the top of the volcano. Good for you!
_____ **17.** word: _____: *n.* all the people born and living at about the same time and having similar experiences; the average period of time between the births of parent and child; bringing into being	(G) You will feel **gratitude** after you have walked through Sulfur Banks. I always feel thankful after I have passed by that foul-smelling area.
_____ **18.** word: _____: *n.* a setting or putting apart; a division	(H) The government is eager to **involve,** or include, people who want to preserve Hawaii Volcanoes National Park.
_____ **19.** word: _____: *v.* to look forward to with fear; *n.* great fear; *adj.* inspiring awe or fear	(I) The national park creates a **separation** between Hilo, a region of Hawaii, and southern Hawaii. The two parts of the island are divided by volcanoes.
_____ **20.** word: _____: *adj.* occurring before something or someone else in time or order	(J) Ruins in the national park show where people lived many **generations** ago.

EXERCISE 3   *Like Meanings and Opposite Meanings* 👉

Directions. For each item below, circle the letter of the choice that means the same, or about the same, as the boldface word.

21. to **caution** about bubbling lava
    - (A) warn
    - (B) inform
    - (C) excite
    - (D) write

22. the **dreaded** Devastation Trail
    - (A) steep
    - (B) isolated
    - (C) awe-inspiring
    - (D) fun

23. the **generation** of steam from the volcano
    - (A) relation
    - (B) bringing forth
    - (C) slowing down
    - (D) explosion

24. to **involve** the Hawaiian government
    - (A) inform
    - (B) invade
    - (C) insult
    - (D) include

25. the **separation** from populated areas
    - (A) tourists
    - (B) pollution
    - (C) setting apart
    - (D) lack of help

Directions. For each item below, circle the letter of the choice that means the opposite, or about the opposite, of the boldface word.

26. to **congratulate** the winner
    - (A) show interest in
    - (B) show feelings for
    - (C) show sorrow for
    - (D) show pleasure for

27. an **error** about Kilauea's elevation
    - (A) correction
    - (B) guideline
    - (C) mistake
    - (D) description

28. with **gratitude** for the wonders of the earth
    - (A) too much concern
    - (B) complete confusion
    - (C) total respect
    - (D) lack of thankfulness

29. the **heroic** mountain climber
    - (A) timid
    - (B) tired
    - (C) brave
    - (D) experienced

30. the **previous** volcanic eruptions
    - (A) ancient
    - (B) dangerous
    - (C) following
    - (D) minor

MAKING NEW WORDS YOUR OWN

Lesson 6 | CONTEXT: Amazing Nature

Going Batty: A Look at the Only True Flying Mammal

Have you ever been afraid of being bitten by a vampire bat when you were outside at night? Well, you will be glad to know that the bats have a bad reputation, not a bad bite. Most bats eat insects, though some eat fish and fruit. The vampire bat does eat blood, but it does not cause serious harm unless it has rabies. In fact, most bats are helpful to human beings. They eat tons of insects every night. In addition, bat guano, or manure, is a valuable fertilizer.

In the following exercises, you will have the opportunity to expand your vocabulary by reading about bats. Below are ten Vocabulary Words that will be used in these exercises.

abdomen	competition	flexible	hoist	mobile
commotion	escort	foe	maximum	paralysis

EXERCISE 1 — Wordbusting ✍️

Directions. Follow these instructions for this word and the nine words on the next page.
- Figure out the word's meaning by looking at its **context**, its **structure**, and its **sound**. Fill in at least one of the three **CSS** boxes. Alternate which boxes you complete.
- Then, look up the word in a dictionary, read all of its meanings, and write the meaning of the word as it is used in the sentence.
- Follow this same process for each of the Vocabulary Words on the next page. You will need to draw your own map for each word. Use a separate sheet of paper.

1.

abdomen → Moths are a favorite food of bats, but they can be hard to catch. Some moths have a pair of primitive ears located near the **abdomen,** the central part of the body. These ears help them hear pursuing bats.

Context:	Structure:	Sound:

Dictionary:

2.
commotion →
Bat colonies are extremely noisy places. Yet, in spite of the **commotion,** mothers are able to locate their young by sound.

3.
competition →
Roosting areas are often very crowded. There is a lot of **competition** for space as each bat struggles to claim its own territory.

4.
escort →
When young bats begin to fly, they are often **escorted** by their mothers, who fly along next to them.

5.
paralysis →
Vampire bats are generally harmless. People used to believe that a bite would cause **paralysis,** making it impossible for the victim to move.

6.
flexible →
Unlike the vampire bat, which eats only blood, most insect-eating bats have a **flexible** diet. They can eat a wide variety of insects, from moths to mosquitoes.

7.
foe →
Bats do not have many enemies because they hang from high, hard-to-get-at places. Snakes, owls, and hawks are **foes** of bats, however.

8.
hoist →
Some bats eat fish. They swoop down on the water, snatch the fish, and **hoist** the fish into the air with their powerful hind claws.

9.
maximum →
How many different kinds of bats are there? The **maximum,** or greatest, number is about nine hundred.

10.
mobile →
Most bats have extremely **mobile** ears and noses. By moving them back and forth, bats are able to hear and smell sources of food.

EXERCISE 2 *Context Clues*

Directions. Scan the definitions in Column A. Then, think about how the boldface words are used in the sentences in Column B. To complete the exercise, match each definition in Column A with the correct Vocabulary Word from Column B. Write the letter of your choice on the line provided. Finally, write the Vocabulary Word on the line before the definition.

COLUMN A	COLUMN B

COLUMN A

_____ **11.** word: _____:
n. the middle part of the body, containing the stomach and other organs; the belly

_____ **12.** word: _____:
v. to lift or pull up; *n.* a tool or piece of equipment used to pull things up

_____ **13.** word: _____:
n. one or more persons who accompany another; *v.* to go with someone

_____ **14.** word: _____:
adj. able to move or change easily; movable

_____ **15.** word: _____:
n. confusion; noisy rushing around; disturbance; violent motion

_____ **16.** word: _____:
n. an enemy

_____ **17.** word: _____:
adj. able to bend without breaking; easily influenced; easily changed

_____ **18.** word: _____:
n. partial or complete loss of a function; a condition in which one cannot act

_____ **19.** word: _____:
n. the greatest amount or number possible or reached; *adj.* greatest possible or reached

_____ **20.** word: _____:
n. rivalry; contest

COLUMN B

(A) Our class visited a bat cave last year. A park ranger was our **escort,** leading us through the cave.

(B) The ranger used a **hoist** to lift us into the cave. Then he moved the equipment aside so that we would not trip over it.

(C) The first time I saw a bat, I couldn't move. The **paralysis** caused by my irrational fear affected my entire body.

(D) Bats are extremely **mobile.** They move easily around obstacles, even when flying very fast.

(E) A bat's fingers support the **flexible** skin of its wings. When the fingers move, the wings can bend also.

(F) As with most mammals, a bat's legs and tail are located below its **abdomen,** or stomach area.

(G) Bats eat insects that are the **foes** of farmers. Farmers hate these insects because the insects damage the crops.

(H) When tracking down fish, fish-eating bats look for **commotion** in the water. Where violent splashing can be seen, a bat's dinner may be nearby.

(I) Bat experts estimate that about 750,000 bats live under the Congress Avenue bridge in Austin, Texas. This is the **maximum** number of bats ever found living in an urban area.

(J) My science class had a **competition** to see how many kinds of bats we could name. I won!

EXERCISE 3 *Like Meanings and Opposite Meanings* ☞

Directions. For each item below, circle the letter of the choice that means the same, or about the same, as the boldface word.

21. a furry **abdomen**
(A) head
(B) foot
(C) tail
(D) belly

22. a **competition** for the best flyer
(A) fight
(B) contest
(C) hunt
(D) reward

23. an experienced **escort**
(A) guide
(B) expert
(C) scientist
(D) worker

24. to **hoist** into the air
(A) push
(B) look up
(C) pull up
(D) fly

25. **paralysis** caused by fear
(A) total panic
(B) loss of movement
(C) extreme worry
(D) confusion

Directions. For each item below, circle the letter of the choice that means the opposite, or about the opposite, of the boldface word.

26. a sudden **commotion**
(A) confusion
(B) peacefulness
(C) movement
(D) mess

27. **flexible** in its diet
(A) movable
(B) unchangeable
(C) inventive
(D) interested

28. an imaginary **foe**
(A) enemy
(B) insect
(C) farmer
(D) friend

29. the **maximum** wingspan
(A) least possible
(B) measurable
(C) greatest possible
(D) wide

30. its **mobile** ears and head
(A) brown
(B) still
(C) furry
(D) movable

MAKING NEW WORDS YOUR OWN

| Lesson 7 | **CONTEXT:** Amazing Nature

Horses: Galloping Through History

Fossil records show that the first horses appeared about fifty million years ago. About six thousand years ago, people began taming horses. That was the start of a long, productive, and friendly relationship. Over the years, horses have carried people in battle, worked their fields, provided transportation, run races, inspired art, and given friendship.

In the following exercises, you will have the opportunity to expand your vocabulary by reading about horses and their relationship to people throughout history. Below are ten Vocabulary Words that will be used in these exercises.

dainty	discourage	inhale	regulate	vacuum
discomfort	earnest	linger	requirement	vault

EXERCISE 1 *Wordbusting*

Directions. Follow these instructions for this word and the nine words on the next page.
- Figure out the word's meaning by looking at its **context**, its **structure**, and its **sound**. Fill in at least one of the three **CSS** boxes. Alternate which boxes you complete.
- Then, look up the word in a dictionary, read all of its meanings, and write the meaning of the word as it is used in the sentence.
- Follow this same process for each of the Vocabulary Words on the next page. You will need to draw your own map for each word. Use a separate sheet of paper.

1.

dainty ⟶ The first horses, now known as *eohippus* ("dawn horse"), were about the size of foxes. They were not **dainty**, though; they did not have delicate features.

Context:	Structure:	Sound:

Dictionary:

2.
discomfort → Greek warriors around 1500 B.C. may have experienced some **discomfort** while riding in horse-drawn chariots. Bumping along on rough roads must have been painful at times.

3.
linger → Even the bravest fighters would not **linger** when they saw a war horse charging at them. Ancient stone carvings show soldiers fleeing from archers shooting arrows while riding fierce-looking horses.

4.
discourage → Christopher Columbus's advisors did not **discourage** him from bringing horses to the New World in 1493, so they were evidently in favor of it.

5.
earnest → When American Indians first saw European horses in the 1400s, their surprise was no doubt **earnest**. Their response was sincere because horses had not been seen in the Americas since 9000 B.C.

6.
inhale → In King Louis XIV's enormous stables at Versailles, a visitor could **inhale** without breathing in unpleasant fumes. The horses were so well cared for that a German prince once said they lived better than he did.

7.
requirement → Before motorized transportation, owning a horse was a **requirement** for many professionals. For example, most doctors had to ride horses while making their rounds to patients.

8.
vacuum → Removing horses from a pioneer's farm certainly would have left a **vacuum**. What other animal could have taken its place?

9.
vault → Horses were once used for mail services, such as the famous Pony Express, because they could run fast and even **vault** obstacles in the roads. For example, the horse's ability to jump over a fallen tree would save the rider time.

10.
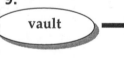 **regulate** → The golden age of horse travel was from 1700 to 1900 in both Europe and North America. During that time, companies were formed to **regulate** and manage the stagecoach systems.

EXERCISE 2   Context Clues

Directions. Scan the definitions in Column A. Then, think about how the boldface words are used in the sentences in Column B. To complete the exercise, match each definition in Column A with the correct Vocabulary Word from Column B. Write the letter of your choice on the line provided. Finally, write the Vocabulary Word on the line before the definition.

COLUMN A	COLUMN B

COLUMN A

_____ **11.** word: _____:
v. to continue to stay; to delay or loiter

_____ **12.** word: _____:
n. uneasiness; minor pain; lack of comfort

_____ **13.** word: _____:
n. an arched ceiling; a secure room for storing valuables; a burial chamber; a jump; *v.* to jump over

_____ **14.** word: _____:
v. to draw into the lungs; to breathe in

_____ **15.** word: _____:
adj. serious; not joking; sincere

_____ **16.** word: _____:
v. to take away courage or confidence; to advise (a person) against something

_____ **17.** word: _____:
n. something that is necessary or demanded; a necessity

_____ **18.** word: _____:
adj. delicate and pretty

_____ **19.** word: _____:
n. a completely empty space; a space left empty by the removal of something usually in it; *v.* to clean with a machine that works by suction

_____ **20.** word: _____:
v. to control, govern, or direct according to rule or system; to adjust to a certain standard

COLUMN B

(A) Knowledge of horses in art is a **requirement** in this class. Also needed is a knowledge of horses in sports.

(B) Throughout history, horses have been subjects of artists. Some paintings portray **dainty** show horses, and others show large , heavy workhorses.

(C) On the arched ceiling is a beautiful painting of horses. The artist used a very tall ladder to reach the **vault** to paint it.

(D) At the museum, I **lingered** to look at the bronze horses created by Frederic Remington while the rest of the group moved on.

(E) The **earnest** guide pointed out how realistic Remington's sculptures are. I could tell that the guide loved his job and took it seriously.

(F) President Andrew Jackson loved racing horses. Not being able to race horses would have left a **vacuum** in his life—a space that politics alone could not have filled.

(G) The best jockeys are confident of their abilities. They are not **discouraged** when they ride horses that have never won.

(H) I would not want to be a jockey because of the **discomfort** of bouncing on a racing horse—it seems very uncomfortable.

(I) Most horses used in polo matches tire after fifteen minutes of play. You can see them **inhale** deeply in frantic attempts to pull air into their lungs.

(J) The temperature must be **regulated** in some stables for the comfort of the horses. Adjusting the temperature is also important for their health.

EXERCISE 3 *Like Meanings and Opposite Meanings* ✍

Directions. For each item below, circle the letter of the choice that means the same, or about the same, as the boldface word.

21. vaulted the hurdle
(A) jumped over
(B) stood on
(C) looked over
(D) sat on

22. a **vacuum** left by a retired racehorse
(A) filled space
(B) deep space
(C) last place
(D) empty space

23. to **regulate** the American quarter horse show
(A) neglect
(B) approve
(C) control
(D) help

24. to **discourage** the young jockey
(A) discover
(B) praise
(C) help out
(D) advise negatively

25. a **requirement** for horse ownership
(A) suggestion
(B) necessity
(C) plan
(D) request

Directions. For each item below, circle the letter of the choice that means the opposite, or about the opposite, of the boldface word.

26. the circus pony's **dainty** costume
(A) new and costly
(B) delicate and pretty
(C) heavy and ugly
(D) old and cheap

27. to **linger** by the Clydesdales
(A) hurry
(B) live
(C) stay
(D) sing

28. the horse's **discomfort**
(A) uneasiness
(B) dance
(C) ease
(D) expression

29. inhaled the dust from the racetrack
(A) breathed in
(B) blinded by
(C) go around
(D) breathed out

30. an **earnest** knight
(A) serious
(B) concerned
(C) joking
(D) happy

MAKING NEW WORDS YOUR OWN

Lesson 8 | **CONTEXT:** Amazing Nature

Texas Dinosaurs

Sixteen different species of dinosaurs once lived in Texas. Some were small, and others were gigantic. Some were quiet plant eaters, and others were fierce meat eaters. They lived a long time ago—65 to 135 million years ago. Their fossils and footprints have been found in three areas of Texas: the Panhandle, North Central to West Texas, and the Big Bend area.

In the following exercises, you will have the opportunity to expand your vocabulary by reading about the dinosaurs of Texas. These ten Vocabulary Words will be used.

acquire	disguise	hibernate	impostor	reference
conceal	gasp	imitate	portion	terminal

EXERCISE 1 *Wordbusting*

Directions. Follow these instructions for this word and the nine words on the next page.
- Figure out the word's meaning by looking at its **context,** its **structure,** and its **sound.** Fill in at least one of the three **CSS** boxes. Alternate which boxes you complete.
- Then, look up the word in a dictionary, read all of its meanings, and write the meaning of the word as it is used in the sentence.
- Follow this same process for each of the Vocabulary Words on the next page. You will need to draw your own map for each word. Use a separate sheet of paper.

1.

(acquire) ⟶ After a museum is able to **acquire** the individual bones of a dinosaur, the hard work begins. Getting the bones is the easy part; it may take many months or even years before the skeleton can be fully assembled.

Context:	Structure:	Sound:

Dictionary:

2.
conceal →
It would have been difficult for the pleurocoelus to **conceal** itself. It weighed thirty-five tons and was fifty feet long.

3.
disguise →
If a chasmosaurus walked into your schoolyard today, would you be able to **disguise** it and keep it a secret? How could you make a seventeen-foot-long creature with a big, bony plate and horns on its head look like anything but a dinosaur?

4.
gasp →
One can imagine the last **gasp** of an animal eaten by deinonychus, the "terrible claw" dinosaur. Its final breath would be drawn in terror.

5.
hibernate →
When dinosaurs lived, Texas was a hot and humid marshland. There would have been no need for dinosaurs to **hibernate,** or go into an inactive state, as some animals do in winter.

6.
imitate →
The acrocanthosaurus, or "high-spined reptile," found in North Central to West Texas, **imitated** the tyrannosaurus by walking and using its claws and teeth in similar ways.

7.
portion →
What **portion** of the body of a tenontosaurus was its tail? More than half of this fifteen-foot-long dinosaur, which once lived in North Central to West Texas, was tail.

8.
impostor →
Don't be fooled by anyone who says he or she is a dinosaur expert and can show you a complete dinosaur skeleton no one else knows about. That person is probably an **impostor**.

9.
reference →
Do you need **reference** material about dinosaurs in Texas? If you do, I can recommend several interesting books.

10.
terminal →
The **terminal** days for dinosaurs came about sixty-five million years ago. There are several theories about what caused them to die out.

EXERCISE 2 *Context Clues* ✍

Directions. Scan the definitions in Column A. Then, think about how the boldface words are used in the sentences in Column B. To complete the exercise, match each definition in Column A with the correct Vocabulary Word from Column B. Write the letter of your choice on the line provided. Finally, write the Vocabulary Word on the line before the definition.

COLUMN A	COLUMN B

COLUMN A

____ **11.** word: _____:
v. to inhale suddenly with surprise; to breathe with difficulty; *n.* a difficult inhalation of breath

____ **12.** word: _____:
v. to gain possession of

____ **13.** word: _____:
v. to give out in parts; *n.* an amount, share, or serving of something

____ **14.** word: _____:
n. a person who deceives others by pretending to be something he or she is not

____ **15.** word: _____:
adj. at the end of something; final; *n.* the ending point; a limit; either end of a transportation line

____ **16.** word: _____:
v. to hide something by changing its usual appearance; *n.* a costume

____ **17.** word: _____:
v. to spend the winter in an inactive state

____ **18.** word: _____:
v. to hide; to keep secret

____ **19.** word: _____:
n. the directing to a source for information; a mention of something or somebody; the naming of a person who can offer recommendation; *v.* to mention a source; *adj.* used or usable for reference

____ **20.** word: _____:
v. to copy exactly; to act the same as

COLUMN B

(A) Whatever event or events caused the end of the dinosaurs, the situation was **terminal.**

(B) Many books about dinosaurs include **references** to Texas dinosaur finds.

(C) Few visitors to the park can **conceal,** or hide, their awe when they see the gigantic footprints.

(D) Artists have **imitated** the tracks at Dinosaur Valley State Park in North Central Texas, but seeing the copies cannot compare with seeing the real tracks.

(E) The scientist responsible for preserving the tracks is R. T. Bird. No one thought he was an **impostor** because it was clear that he was a true authority on dinosaur fossils.

(F) To create a model of a dinosaur, an artist must **acquire** knowledge about the creatures. It takes much study for an artist to get enough information to correctly duplicate a dinosaur.

(G) Children often **gasp** when they suddenly see the big models of dinosaurs at the park. After their surprise, the children run to see the dinosaurs up close.

(H) Park rangers **portion** the information they share, so visitors will not be overwhelmed with too much knowledge at once.

(I) Experts argue over whether dinosaurs were warm- or coldblooded, but no one believes they **hibernated** in cold weather, like some modern-day reptiles.

(J) A dinosaur costume would be an excellent **disguise!**

EXERCISE 3 *Like Meanings and Opposite Meanings*

Directions. For each item below, circle the letter of the choice that means the same, or about the same, as the boldface word.

21. **gasped** at seeing the dinosaur
    (A) exhaled slowly
    (B) smiled broadly
    (C) inhaled suddenly
    (D) laughed loudly

22. to **hibernate** like some mammals
    (A) spend winter in an inactive state
    (B) spend summer in an active state
    (C) spend winter in a southern state
    (D) spend fall in a restless state

23. to **acquire** knowledge
    (A) remember
    (B) lose
    (C) maintain
    (D) gain

24. your **reference** to a dinosaur egg
    (A) decision about
    (B) mention of
    (C) discovery of
    (D) talk of

25. a good Tyrannosaurus **disguise**
    (A) drawing
    (B) statue
    (C) body
    (D) costume

Directions. For each item below, circle the letter of the choice that means the opposite, or about the opposite, of the boldface word.

26. a **portion** of a dinosaur fossil
    (A) whole
    (B) picture
    (C) part
    (D) likeness

27. **conceals** the fossil
    (A) keeps
    (B) hides
    (C) shows
    (D) takes

28. fossils sold by an **impostor**
    (A) deceiving, pretending person
    (B) doubting, sly person
    (C) honest, real person
    (D) unruly, dishonest person

29. the **terminal** footprint
    (A) first
    (B) final
    (C) second
    (D) greatest

30. **imitated** a flying reptile
    (A) followed the example of
    (B) pretended to be
    (C) searched for
    (D) acted differently from

MAKING NEW WORDS YOUR OWN

Lesson 9 | CONTEXT: Amazing Nature
Weird Weather: El Niño

Even in one place, no two years have exactly the same weather. Snow may pile high one year and not fall at all the next. One summer may be hotter than most others. One important factor in global weather variation is El Niño, a warm water current that occurs every few years in the Pacific Ocean. This warm current causes dramatic changes in weather around the world.

In the following exercises, you will have the opportunity to expand your vocabulary by reading about El Niño and other mysterious weather phenomena. Below are ten Vocabulary Words that will be used.

bombard	lunar	pharmacy	receipt	static
bureau	particle	pierce	resign	surgery

EXERCISE 1 *Wordbusting*

Directions. Follow these instructions for this word and the nine words on the next page.
- Figure out the word's meaning by looking at its **context,** its **structure,** and its **sound.** Fill in at least one of the three **CSS** boxes. Alternate which boxes you complete.
- Then, look up the word in a dictionary, read all of its meanings, and write the meaning of the word as it is used in the sentence.
- Follow this same process for each of the Vocabulary Words on the next page. You will need to draw your own map for each word. Use a separate sheet of paper.

1.

bombard → While we are being **bombarded** with weather reports on the radio and television, we often do not understand the causes of weather patterns.

Context:

Structure:

Sound:

Dictionary:

2.
bureau →

The National Weather Service is a government department that predicts and studies the weather. Scientists at the weather **bureau** do not yet understand what causes El Niño. For this reason, they cannot always predict when the next El Niño will occur.

3.
lunar →

Lunar attraction, or the gravitational pull of the moon, causes ocean tides. The moon does not have much effect on ocean currents such as El Niño, however.

4.
particle →

A water **particle** that is caught up in an ocean tide will be carried either towards or away from the shore as the moon pulls the tide. However, if that same small molecule of water is caught in a current, it will be carried along in the current's flow instead.

5.
pierce →

When El Niño **pierces** the normally cool waters of South America's Pacific coast, disasterous changes occur. The effect of the warm current passing into cold waters damages ocean life there.

6.
pharmacy →

Plants and animals in the sea are affected by El Niño. Some of these organisms are of value to students of **pharmacy**. Pharmacists use some sea organisms to prepare drugs and medicines.

7.
receipt →

The jet stream has a major effect on world climates. For this reason, scientists are always eager for **receipt** of information about El Niño. Getting such news at the right time can help them predict weather trends.

8.
resign →

El Niño affects rainfall around the world. In 1991, the current caused severe flooding in parts of Texas. As the rains continued, many Texans had to **resign** themselves to, or accept, the fact that their homes were gone forever.

9.
static →

The 1998 flooding in Somalia occurred because El Niño caused severe rains that lasted for some time. When a weather system is **static,** the weather in an area remains unchanged for a long time.

10.
surgery →

The floods caused many injuries. As a result, doctors spent more time than usual in **surgery,** performing operations.

EXERCISE 2 *Context Clues*

Directions. Scan the definitions in Column A. Then, think about how the boldface words are used in the sentences in Column B. To complete the exercise, match each definition in Column A with the correct Vocabulary Word from Column B. Write the letter of your choice on the line provided. Finally, write the Vocabulary Word on the line before the definition.

COLUMN A	COLUMN B
_____ **11.** word: _____: *v.* to pass into or through; to stab; to sharply affect the senses or feelings	(A) My Uncle Ramón is a fisherman who lives in Arica, Chile. He suffers from arthritis. The pain is severe, but it cannot be helped by **surgery**.
_____ **12.** word: _____: *n.* an operation; the operating room	(B) A friend of his owns a **pharmacy,** and Uncle Ramón went to her drugstore to get medicine for his pain.
_____ **13.** word: _____: *n.* a chest of drawers; an agency, usually one that gives and collects information; a government department	(C) When he arrived, no one was there. Hearing **static** coming from a radio, he followed the crackling sound to the back room. The clerk there told Uncle Ramón that news of El Niño had just arrived.
_____ **14.** word: _____: *n.* a receiving; proof of receiving	(D) Uncle Ramón bought some arthritis medicine, and the clerk handed Uncle Ramón a sales slip. Walking outside, Uncle Ramón stuffed the **receipt** for his medicine in his pocket.
_____ **15.** word: _____: *v.* to leave or offer to leave one's job or office; to accept something passively	(E) He felt the first raindrops **pierce** through his shirt. "I should have known," he thought, feeling the cold water on his skin. "My hands always hurt before a storm."
_____ **16.** word: _____: *n.* a very small piece; a slight trace	(F) "Now we must **resign** ourselves to a poor fishing season. We must accept that El Niño will warm the ocean and kill many fish."
_____ **17.** word: _____: *v.* to attack verbally; to attack with bombs or to fire at with projectiles	(G) Uncle Ramón knew that he would be **bombarded** with questions when he got home. Aunt Nina would scold him for going out in a storm and ask him for news from town.
_____ **18.** word: _____: *n.* electrical discharges in the atmosphere that produce radio or television interference; *adj.* not moving; still	(H) Arriving home, he placed his medicine in one of the drawers of his **bureau,** or dresser.
_____ **19.** word: _____: *n.* the profession of preparing and dispensing medicines; a drugstore	(I) Through a window, he stared grimly at the gloomy, **lunar** paleness of the day outside. The gray landscape was veiled with rain.
_____ **20.** word: _____: *adj.* of or on the moon; like the moon	(J) Rain was washing away nearly every **particle** of his hope for good fishing.

EXERCISE 3 *Like Meanings and Opposite Meanings* 🖎

Directions. For each item below, circle the letter of the choice that means the same, or about the same, as the boldface word.

21. to study **pharmacy**
 (A) business finance
 (B) medicines
 (C) the rulers of ancient Egypt
 (D) crop growing

22. an old **bureau**
 (A) long tunnel
 (B) chest of drawers
 (C) den
 (D) company of friends

23. emergency **surgery**
 (A) vehicle for transporting injured people
 (B) plan of action
 (C) attack
 (D) operation

24. the **lunar** timetable
 (A) of the ocean
 (B) of the sun
 (C) of the moon
 (D) impossible

25. to **pierce** their defenses
 (A) cut through
 (B) repair
 (C) prepare
 (D) calm down

Directions. For each item below, circle the letter of the choice that means the opposite, or about the opposite, of the boldface word.

26. the **particles** of glass
 (A) large, whole pieces
 (B) thin layers
 (C) tiny bits
 (D) cups and pitchers

27. to **resign** his position
 (A) accept
 (B) change
 (C) formally place a signature
 (D) improve

28. to **bombard** the fort
 (A) attack
 (B) build
 (C) float
 (D) defend

29. a **static** situation
 (A) active
 (B) hopeless
 (C) a measure of performance
 (D) statewide

30. due on **receipt**
 (A) availability
 (B) sending
 (C) request
 (D) a specific day

▼

MAKING NEW WORDS YOUR OWN

| Lesson 10 | ### CONTEXT: Amazing Nature

Mark Twain's Mighty Mississippi

The *Adventures of Huckleberry Finn* by Mark Twain (1835–1910) tells the story of a boy living near the Mississippi River before the Civil War. Like Huck, Mark Twain, whose real name was Samuel Clemens, grew up along the Mississippi. He worked for a time as a riverboat pilot, but he is most famous for his writing.

In the following exercises, you will have the opportunity to expand your vocabulary by reading about Mark Twain's Mississippi. Below are ten Vocabulary Words that will be used in these exercises.

conviction	gossip	license	ransom	suspicion
flammable	jeopardy	pry	stray	toll

EXERCISE 1 *Wordbusting* 🖎

Directions. Follow these instructions for this word and the nine words on the next page.
- Figure out the word's meaning by looking at its **context,** its **structure,** and its **sound.** Fill in at least one of the three **CSS** boxes. Alternate which boxes you complete.
- Then, look up the word in a dictionary, read all of its meanings, and write the meaning of the word as it is used in the sentence.
- Follow this same process for each of the Vocabulary Words on the next page. You will need to draw your own map for each word. Use a separate sheet of paper.

1.

(conviction) ⟶ In *Adventures of Huckleberry Finn,* Huck pretends to be Tom Sawyer. In real life, a person pretending to be someone else could face **conviction** and spend time in jail.

Context:	Structure:	Sound:

Dictionary:

2.

gossip → When he was a boy, Twain loved to hear people **gossip**. He especially enjoyed rumors and tall tales told by people who had traveled on the Mississippi.

3.

license → Twain longed to work on a steamboat. He felt that working on the river would give him the **license** to be free and independent.

4.

pry → While traveling down the Mississippi River, Twain managed to convince a pilot to teach him how to steer a steamboat. However, it was not easy to **pry** the knowledge out of the pilot.

5.

 → Mississippi steamboats were powered by boilers. **Flammable** materials, such as wood or coal, were burned in the boilers.

6.

 → After the Civil War, steamboats were replaced by the railroad. The change took a **toll** on the small riverside towns, which lost money because they depended on the steamboats for trade.

7.

 → When he was eighteen, Mark Twain decided that he wanted to wander for a while. He **strayed** from Missouri to New York and Philadelphia and then finally returned to the Mississippi River.

8.

jeopardy → Twain's finances were in **jeopardy** when he lost a great deal of money in investments between 1881 and 1894.

9.

 → Twain also lost money when his publishing company failed in 1894. He was left with a debt that seemed as high as the **ransom** for the release of a king.

10.

 → Toward the end of his life, Twain developed a strong **suspicion** of people. He seemed to believe that people in general were greedy and untrustworthy.

EXERCISE 2 *Context Clues* ✍

Directions. Scan the definitions in Column A. Then, think about how the boldface words are used in the sentences in Column B. To complete the exercise, match each definition in Column A with the correct Vocabulary Word from Column B. Write the letter of your choice on the line provided. Finally, write the Vocabulary Word on the line before the definition.

COLUMN A	COLUMN B

COLUMN A

_____ **11.** word: _____:
v. to wander from a place; to fail to concentrate; *adj.* wandering; lost; lone; *n.* person or thing that wanders or is lost

_____ **12.** word: _____:
n. in danger; at risk

_____ **13.** word: _____:
n. a charge for; a fare; an amount lost or taken; *v.* to ring a bell slowly

_____ **14.** word: _____:
n. formal permission; a legal document giving formal permission; *v.* to give permission formally

_____ **15.** word: _____:
v. to raise or move by force; to obtain with difficulty; to peer or snoop; *n.* a tool for raising or moving something

_____ **16.** word: _____:
n. the act of suspecting guilt; tending to cause others to believe or suspect guilt

_____ **17.** word: _____:
n. holding strongly to a belief; convinced; being found legally guilty of a crime

_____ **18.** word: _____:
n. a person who spreads rumors; idle talk or rumors; *v.* to spread rumors

_____ **19.** word: _____:
n. the price paid for the release of a hostage; *v.* to pay money for such a release

_____ **20.** word: _____:
adj. easily set on fire

COLUMN B

(A) Twain received his pilot's **license** in 1859. This permit gave him permission to operate steamboats.

(B) Steamboats were made out of wood. This means that they were **flammable** and burned easily.

(C) During the years that Mark Twain was a riverboat pilot, lives were often in **jeopardy** due to steamboat boiler explosions.

(D) To make river travel less dangerous, the government sent boats to **pry,** or remove, obstacles from the water.

(E) The **toll** for traveling on the river was low when Twain was alive. Now it costs much more.

(F) The Mississippi River is badly polluted to-day. Many people have a **suspicion** that some industries are dumping dangerous materials into the river illegally.

(G) Twain became a **stray** again after the Civil War began in 1861. He wandered all over the United States and Europe.

(H) Twain was a humorous **gossip** who loved to tell stories about his years on the Mississippi.

(I) Twain held a **conviction** about humor. He deeply believed that humor could illustrate certain human qualities and actions.

(J) In *The Adventures of Tom Sawyer*, Tom and Huck discover a treasure. They find enough money to **ransom** a dozen hostages.

EXERCISE 3 *Like Meanings and Opposite Meanings* 👈

Directions. For each item below, circle the letter of the choice that means the same, or about the same, as the boldface word.

21. putting lives in **jeopardy**
 (A) comfortable surroundings
 (B) an unsafe situation
 (C) a safe situation
 (D) order

22. a **license** to operate a boat
 (A) permission
 (B) training
 (C) desire
 (D) request

23. to express a **conviction**
 (A) doubt
 (B) desire
 (C) belief
 (D) promise

24. to **ransom** the captives
 (A) kidnap
 (B) injure seriously
 (C) pay to release
 (D) frighten terribly

25. to **toll** a bell
 (A) study
 (B) ring
 (C) cast out
 (D) repair

Directions. For each item below, circle the letter of the choice that means the opposite, or about the opposite, of the boldface word.

26. a **flammable** fuel
 (A) expensive
 (B) fireproof
 (C) smelly
 (D) hot

27. the **gossip** about life on the river
 (A) serious discussion
 (B) bad news
 (C) rumors
 (D) idle talk

28. to **pry** into personal affairs
 (A) ask about
 (B) stay out of
 (C) fall
 (D) snoop

29. the **stray** cat that begs for food
 (A) lost
 (B) beautiful
 (C) unhappy
 (D) homebound

30. a **suspicion** that it will rain
 (A) knowledge
 (B) guess
 (C) worry
 (D) bet

MAKING NEW WORDS YOUR OWN

Lesson 11 CONTEXT: People and Places

Checking Out the Chimps with Jane Goodall

From the time she was a little girl, Jane Goodall (b. 1934) wanted to work with animals. When she grew up, she became an ethologist—someone who studies animal behavior. She worked with Louis Leakey, who was studying animals and early humans. In 1960, Jane Goodall began studying chimpanzees in Gombe, Tanzania. She became very close to several individual chimpanzees and was able to correct many misunderstandings about the animals.

In the following exercises, you will have the opportunity to expand your vocabulary by reading about Jane Goodall. These ten Vocabulary Words will be used.

analyze	debate	essential	offspring	reaction
career	document	identical	publicity	thorough

EXERCISE 1 *Wordbusting*

Directions. Follow these instructions for this word and the nine words on the next page.
- Figure out the word's meaning by looking at its **context,** its **structure,** and its **sound.** Fill in at least one of the three **CSS** boxes. Alternate which boxes you complete.
- Then, look up the word in a dictionary, read all of its meanings, and write the meaning of the word as it is used in the sentence.
- Follow this same process for each of the Vocabulary Words on the next page. You will need to draw your own map for each word. Use a separate sheet of paper.

1.

analyze → In order to **analyze** the behavior of chimpanzees, Jane Goodall decided to live with them. This allowed her to examine their actions in detail.

Context:

Structure:

Sound:

Dictionary:

2.
career → Jane Goodall began her **career** working as a secretary. Soon she was able to begin working with animals, something she had always wanted to do.

3.
thorough → Louis Leakey supported Goodall because he knew she was **thorough**. He believed that only someone who was very exact and who paid close attention to details should do the study.

4.
debate → Jane Goodall **debated** with scientists who did not believe that chimps would eat meat. She argued her case by showing them evidence.

5.
document → Every night, Goodall wrote in her journal about her experiences with the chimpanzees. She wanted to **document** everything she had seen during the day.

6.
essential → An **essential** for Goodall was a good pair of binoculars. Without them, she would have had trouble with her research.

7.
identical → Humans and chimpanzees have some **identical** features. For instance, chimpanzees have thumbs that are almost exactly like human thumbs.

8.
offspring → Goodall realized that most chimps travel in small groups. She also noticed that mothers usually carry their young **offspring** under their bodies.

9.
publicity → Goodall received a lot of **publicity** because of her work with chimpanzees. This public attention helped her raise money for her research.

10.
reaction → When Goodall first began to study chimpanzees, they were afraid of her. She was not concerned about their **reaction** because she believed they would soon respond with trust.

EXERCISE 2   *Context Clues*

Directions. Scan the definitions in Column A. Then, think about how the boldface words are used in the sentences in Column B. To complete the exercise, match each definition in Column A with the correct Vocabulary Word from Column B. Write the letter of your choice on the line provided. Finally, write the Vocabulary Word on the line before the definition.

COLUMN A

_____ **11.** word: _____:
adj. necessary; *n.* something that is necessary; a necessary element

_____ **12.** word: _____:
adj. done from beginning to end; complete; painstakingly accurate

_____ **13.** word: _____:
n. any material which makes something known to the public; public attention

_____ **14.** word: _____:
v. to argue; to take part in a formal discussion; *n.* the discussion of a question

_____ **15.** word: _____:
adj. exactly alike; duplicate

_____ **16.** word: _____:
n. a response to something

_____ **17.** word: _____:
n. a written record; *v.* to provide as proof or support

_____ **18.** word: _____:
n. the work one does all one's life; a job; rapid progress; *v.* to move at full speed; to rush; *adj.* pursuing an activity as a life's work

_____ **19.** word: _____:
n. a child or a young animal; a result; descendant

_____ **20.** word: _____:
v. to examine in detail; to study the nature of something

COLUMN B

(A) Money was **essential** to Goodall's research. Without funding, she would not have been able to continue her research.

(B) Although people may think that all chimps are **identical,** individual chimps are quite different in their appearances and actions.

(C) Jane Goodall was interested in **analyzing,** or looking closely at, the relationships between male and female chimpanzees.

(D) Once, Goodall was startled by three chimpanzees **careering** through the forest. As they raced by, they bared their teeth at her.

(E) How did the chimps respond when Jane Goodall's son was born? Their **reaction** was one of curiosity.

(F) Jane Goodall discovered that female chimps have only one baby, or **offspring,** every five or six years.

(G) Jane Goodall is **thorough** when she studies the chimpanzees. She records every detail about them.

(H) Written **documents** by Jane Goodall and her assistants in Africa are studied by students of animal behavior.

(I) Jane Goodall often speaks in the United States. Advance **publicity** lets people know when and where she will speak.

(J) The **debate** about how to protect the chimpanzees continues. It is a good sign, though, that people care enough to discuss the question.

EXERCISE 3 *Like Meanings and Opposite Meanings*

Directions. For each item below, circle the letter of the choice that means the same, or about the same, as the boldface word.

21. to **analyze** animal communication
  (A) listen to
  (B) examine
  (C) understand
  (D) be a part of

22. Louis Leakey's **document**
  (A) degree
  (B) written record
  (C) life story
  (D) spoken word

23. the **offspring** of a discussion
  (A) parents
  (B) topic
  (C) result
  (D) wish

24. **publicity** about Jane Goodall's research
  (A) public attention
  (B) funding for
  (C) magazines
  (D) tough questions

25. the chimp's **reaction**
  (A) call
  (B) curiosity
  (C) fear
  (D) response

Directions. For each item below, circle the letter of the choice that means the opposite, or about the opposite, of the boldface word.

26. a **career** animal expert
  (A) angry
  (B) lonely
  (C) occasional
  (D) responsible

27. to **debate** environmental issues
  (A) agree on
  (B) argue about
  (C) outline
  (D) explain

28. an **identical** response
  (A) the same
  (B) unusual
  (C) opposite
  (D) poor

29. **essential** for health
  (A) required
  (B) unnecessary
  (C) meaningful
  (D) prescribed

30. a **thorough** study
  (A) expensive
  (B) correct
  (C) humorous
  (D) incomplete

MAKING NEW WORDS YOUR OWN

Lesson 12 **CONTEXT: People and Places**

Looking for Green Gables: Anne's Prince Edward Island

Anne Shirley is the title character of the novel *Anne of Green Gables* by Lucy Maud Montgomery (1874–1942). Anne is like her creator in many ways. Both lived on and loved Prince Edward Island, Canada's smallest province. Many tourists come to the island to see its beauty and to visit the house used as the model for Anne's house, Green Gables.

In the following exercises, you will have the opportunity to expand your vocabulary by reading about Anne of Green Gables and Prince Edward Island. Below are ten Vocabulary Words that will be used in these exercises.

biography	determination	notion	respectable	scholar
destination	generous	profession	routine	self-confidence

EXERCISE 1 *Wordbusting*

Directions. Follow these instructions for this word and the nine words on the next page.
- Figure out the word's meaning by looking at its **context,** its **structure,** and its **sound.** Fill in at least one of the three **CSS** boxes. Alternate which boxes you complete.
- Then, look up the word in a dictionary, read all of its meanings, and write the meaning of the word as it is used in the sentence.
- Follow this same process for each of the Vocabulary Words on the next page. You will need to draw your own map for each word. Use a separate sheet of paper.

1.

(biography) ⟶ Any **biography** of Lucy Maud Montgomery includes information about Prince Edward Island. Known as P.E.I., the island is a major part of her life's story.

Context:

Structure:

Sound:

Dictionary:

2.
destination →

I had long wanted to go to P.E.I. because I had read all eight of the Anne books and the story of Montgomery's life. When I set out on my vacation last summer, the island was my **destination**.

3.
determination →

My **determination** to go to P.E.I., which is located in the Gulf of St. Lawrence, was great. I also had a firm intention to visit all the places described in the Anne novels.

4.
generous →

A **generous** aunt gave me money to go to P.E.I. She showed me pictures that she had taken of Prince Edward Island National Park.

5.
notion →

Once actually on P.E.I., I had the **notion** to drive around and look at the farms. It was a good idea, because many farmers were out harvesting the potatoes for which the island is famous.

6.
profession →

Farming is one of the main **professions** on the island, which has extremely rich red soil. Another popular occupation is fishing, especially fishing for lobsters and oysters.

7.
respectable →

The Prince Edward Island lobster is a **respectable** meal. I went to a community lobster dinner where I had plenty of oysters that were also of excellent quality.

8.
routine →

At the dinner, some local children put on an entertaining **routine** based on *Anne of Green Gables*. Of course, a red-haired girl played Anne in the skit and pretended not to like the color of her hair.

9.
scholar →

I was lucky to meet a woman who was a real *Anne of Green Gables* **scholar**. She offered to share her vast knowledge with me.

10.
self-confidence →

My new friend said she admired Anne's **self-confidence**. She said that reading the Anne books had helped her to become more sure of herself.

EXERCISE 2 *Context Clues*

Directions. Scan the definitions in Column A. Then, think about how the boldface words are used in the sentences in Column B. To complete the exercise, match each definition in Column A with the correct Vocabulary Word from Column B. Write the letter of your choice on the line provided. Finally, write the Vocabulary Word on the line before the definition.

COLUMN A	COLUMN B

COLUMN A

_____ **11.** word: _____:
n. a whim; an idea; a vague thought

_____ **12.** word: _____:
n. a belief in oneself and one's abilities

_____ **13.** word: _____:
n. a firm intention; firmness of purpose

_____ **14.** word: _____:
adj. worthy of esteem; proper; fairly good in quality or quantity

_____ **15.** word: _____:
n. the story of a person's life

_____ **16.** word: _____:
adj. willing to give or share; unselfish; ample

_____ **17.** word: _____:
n. the place toward which someone or something is going

_____ **18.** word: _____:
n. an occupation; a declaration

_____ **19.** word: _____:
n. a learned or knowledgeable person; a student

_____ **20.** word: _____:
n. a regular procedure; a custom; a theatrical skit; *adj.* occurring on a regular basis

COLUMN B

(A) I didn't plan my activities on P.E.I. but acted on whim. A sudden **notion** to see Charlottetown, the island's capital, resulted in lots of fun.

(B) I had a **determination** to see the village of Cavendish. It was my purpose to go to the place called Avonlea in Montgomery's books.

(C) The house called Green Gables once belonged to Montgomery's cousins, a **respectable** brother and sister who ran an equally proper farm.

D) I wonder if they were as **generous** as the unselfish brother and sister, Matthew and Marilla, who welcomed Anne.

(E) When touring the house, I could imagine Anne's summer **routine** as a child. Each day she helped in the kitchen, wrote, and daydreamed.

(F) I think working at Green Gables for the Canadian park service would be a wonderful **profession**. All my reading should be good background for such a career.

(G) After I went through Green Gables, Anne's Haunted Woods nearby was my next **destination**.

(H) P.E.I. is where both Montgomery and Anne learned to believe in themselves. I could feel their **self-confidence** there.

(I) When I was in college, a fellow **scholar** once told me that the Micmacs, an American Indian people, lived on Prince Edward Island.

(J) I later read a **biography** of the French explorer Jacques Cartier, who came to the island in 1534. The account of his life is fascinating.

EXERCISE 3 *Like Meanings and Opposite Meanings* ✍

Directions. For each item below, circle the letter of the choice that means the same, or about the same, as the boldface word.

21. a **respectable** Canadian author
  (A) favorite
  (B) disliked
  (C) famous
  (D) esteemed

22. the teaching **profession**
  (A) equipment
  (B) community
  (C) occupation
  (D) work force

23. a Canadian **scholar**
  (A) person who studies
  (B) person who coaches
  (C) person who drives
  (D) person who fishes

24. a **notion** to paint a landscape
  (A) hope
  (B) chance
  (C) order
  (D) idea

25. reading a **biography**
  (A) story about the history of Canada
  (B) story of a person's life
  (C) map
  (D) list of a writer's books

Directions. For each item below, circle the letter of the choice that means the opposite, or about the opposite, of the boldface word.

26. **routine** tours of Green Gables
  (A) unpredictable
  (B) regular
  (C) hourly
  (D) enjoyable

27. a **generous** donation to Parks Canada
  (A) welcome
  (B) unwelcome
  (C) selfish
  (D) unselfish

28. a feeling of **determination**
  (A) purposelessness
  (B) firmness
  (C) unusualness
  (D) originality

29. an island **destination**
  (A) view
  (B) starting point
  (C) end point
  (D) summer storm

30. a writer's **self-confidence**
  (A) belief in oneself
  (B) concern over finishing a book
  (C) lack of faith in oneself
  (D) hope in the ability to create

MAKING NEW WORDS YOUR OWN

Lesson 13 | CONTEXT: People and Places

If You Like Peanut Butter, Thank George Washington Carver

Imagine life without peanut butter! George Washington Carver (1864–1943) was a scientist who developed more than three hundred products from the peanut. Carver was born into slavery. He eventually went to college and later joined the faculty of Tuskegee Institute. His interest in the peanut caused it to become a major part of agriculture in the South.

In the following exercises, you will have the opportunity to expand your vocabulary by reading about George Washington Carver. Below are ten Vocabulary Words that will be used in these exercises.

ceremony	consent	ignite	management	quarantine
conduct	fragrant	interrupt	plead	scheme

EXERCISE 1 Wordbusting

Directions. Follow these instructions for this word and the nine words on the next page.
- Figure out the word's meaning by looking at its **context,** its **structure,** and its **sound.** Fill in at least one of the three **CSS** boxes. Alternate which boxes you complete.
- Then, look up the word in a dictionary, read all of its meanings, and write the meaning of the word as it is used in the sentence.
- Follow this same process for each of the Vocabulary Words on the next page. You will need to draw your own map for each word. Use a separate sheet of paper.

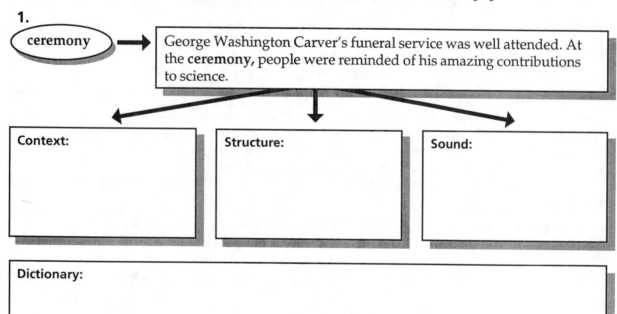

1.

ceremony → George Washington Carver's funeral service was well attended. At the **ceremony,** people were reminded of his amazing contributions to science.

Context:

Structure:

Sound:

Dictionary:

2.

consent ➔ In 1896, Carver **consented,** or agreed, to direct the department of agriculture at Tuskegee Institute. He conducted most of his research at Tuskegee from 1896 until his death.

3.

conduct ➔ Carver **conducted** hundreds of experiments in his lab. Under his direction, many products were developed.

4.

ignite ➔ Carver's laboratory equipment included burners for heating. It was important to **ignite** the burners carefully to avoid setting a fire.

5.

fragrant ➔ Peanut milk was one of Carver's first widely used inventions. The **fragrant,** sweet-smelling liquid was a substitute for cow's milk.

6.

interrupt ➔ Carver testified before a committee of Congress in 1921. The committee was so interested in his unusual peanut products that they frequently **interrupted** his talk to ask questions.

7.

management ➔ Carver helped the peanut industry in the South. The **management** of various companies asked for his help with a variety of problems. The business directors appreciated Carver's knowledge.

8.

plead ➔ If Carver had ever threatened to leave Tuskegee Institute, its directors probably would have **pleaded** with him, begging him to stay.

9.

quarantine ➔ Carver worked with some plants that were diseased. He had to **quarantine** these plants by setting them apart from the others. Then the other plants would not catch the diseases.

10.

scheme ➔ Carver's **scheme** was for southern farmers to be more productive. He planned to provide them more possibilities.

EXERCISE 2 *Context Clues* ✍

Directions. Scan the definitions in Column A. Then, think about how the boldface words are used in the sentences in Column B. To complete the exercise, match each definition in Column A with the correct Vocabulary Word from Column B. Write the letter of your choice on the line provided. Finally, write the Vocabulary Word on the line before the definition.

COLUMN A	COLUMN B

COLUMN A

_____ **11.** word: _____:
n. behavior; *v.* to lead; to direct

_____ **12.** word: _____:
n. a carefully arranged plan; a plot; an orderly combination of things; *v.* to construct a plan; to plot

_____ **13.** word: _____:
n. an isolation or restriction of movement to keep disease from spreading; *v.* to set apart

_____ **14.** word: _____:
v. to set on fire; to start burning; to excite

_____ **15.** word: _____:
n. a formal act or ritual; the service at which such an act is performed

_____ **16.** word: _____:
v. to break in upon; to stop or obstruct

_____ **17.** word: _____:
v. to agree with; to give approval or permission for something; *n.* an agreement; permission

_____ **18.** word: _____:
adj. having a pleasant smell; sweet-smelling

_____ **19.** word: _____:
v. to offer as an excuse; to declare oneself in court to be guilty or not guilty; to beg

_____ **20.** word: _____:
n. the act of controlling; one or more persons who direct a group or business

COLUMN B

(A) George Washington Carver was frequently sick when he was a boy. He was often **quarantined,** or kept apart, from other children.

(B) Carver would sometimes **interrupt** his work in the lab to stop and research new ideas.

(C) Carver **schemed** to make crop rotation, the planting of different crops in different seasons, a common practice. Farmers who followed Carver's plan found that all their crops improved.

(D) One of Carver's inventions was a kind of soap made from peanuts. The soap had a pleasing, **fragrant** smell.

(E) A popular speaker, Carver was in great demand. Organizations such as schools and the YMCA **pleaded** with him to speak to them.

(F) When he traveled, Carver often left the **management,** or direction, of his experiments to other scientists.

(G) Carver was well known for his polite **conduct**. His behavior was imitated by many of his students.

(H) Carver was a champion of the rights of African Americans. He often **ignited** passions and made people eager for justice.

(I) Carver asked some of his students to write to him after they left Tuskegee Institute. Most of them were glad to **consent**. They readily agreed to keep in touch.

(J) Without **ceremony,** Carver often led informal nature tours.

EXERCISE 3 *Like Meanings and Opposite Meanings* ☞

Directions. For each item below, circle the letter of the choice that means the same, or about the same, as the boldface word.

21. a formal **ceremony**
(A) ritual
(B) classroom
(C) statement
(D) suit

22. to **interrupt** suddenly
(A) finish
(B) break in
(C) inform
(D) find

23. to **plead** ignorance
(A) avoid
(B) overcome
(C) find the cause of
(D) explain

24. to **conduct** an experiment
(A) be the leader of
(B) follow after
(C) create a design for
(D) carry through

25. a **scheme** to find more uses for peanuts
(A) grant
(B) plan
(C) lab
(D) reason

Directions. For each item below, circle the letter of the choice that means the opposite, or about the opposite, of the boldface word.

26. **quarantined** for a short time
(A) mixed in
(B) ill
(C) kept apart
(D) healthy

27. to **consent** to do more research
(A) hope
(B) plan
(C) dream
(D) refuse

28. a **fragrant** flower
(A) stinking
(B) yellow
(C) sweet
(D) blooming

29. to **ignite** a match
(A) light
(B) put out
(C) freeze
(D) steam

30. the industry's **management**
(A) workers
(B) scientists
(C) bosses
(D) teachers

MAKING NEW WORDS YOUR OWN

Lesson 14 | CONTEXT: People and Places

Just Where Did *the Red Fern Grow? Appalachia . . .*

Wilson Rawls's (1913–1984) *Where the Red Fern Grows* is a story of love and triumph. A boy forms a deep friendship with two dogs who give their lives to save him from danger. The young-adult novel is set in Appalachia, a region in the southeastern mountains of the United States. This area has some of the country's most beautiful scenery. Every year, thousands of hikers walk along the Appalachian Trail, which runs for more than two thousand miles between Georgia and Maine.

In the following exercises, you will have the opportunity to expand your vocabulary by reading about Appalachia. These ten Vocabulary Words will be used.

architect	desperate	eternal	realm	victim
betray	district	glimpse	sacrifice	victorious

EXERCISE 1   *Wordbusting* ✍

Directions. Follow these instructions for this word and the nine words on the next page.
- Figure out the word's meaning by looking at its **context,** its **structure,** and its **sound.** Fill in at least one of the three **CSS** boxes. Alternate which boxes you complete.
- Then, look up the word in a dictionary, read all of its meanings, and write the meaning of the word as it is used in the sentence.
- Follow this same process for each of the Vocabulary Words on the next page. You will need to draw your own map for each word. Use a separate sheet of paper.

1.

(architect) → Special cabins and lodges for hikers can be found along the Appalachian Trail. **Architects** designed these buildings to be simple and comfortable.

Context:	Structure:	Sound:

Dictionary:

2.

betray →

The hounds Old Dan and Little Ann in *Where the Red Fern Grows* would never turn against their owner. They were too faithful to **betray** him.

3.

eternal →

The theme of the book is an **eternal,** or everlasting, one—the close relationships that develop between humans and animals.

4.

victim →

The narrator of *Where the Red Fern Grows* is seriously injured when he becomes the **victim** of a mountain lion attack.

5.

sacrifice →

Old Dan and Little Ann make a **sacrifice** for their owner: They give up their lives to save him.

6.

desperate →

As many young people leave Appalachia for jobs in cities, their hometown citizens may become **desperate**. How will the towns survive without young people?

7.

district →

The Appalachian Trail is over two thousand miles long. It passes through many **districts**, running through county after county and state after state from Maine to Georgia.

8.

glimpse →

Driving on the Blue Ridge Parkway, one can **glimpse** secluded mountain meadows. A driver should not be tempted to take a longer look, though, because the road is high and winding!

9.

victorious →

People concerned about the environment have been at least partially **victorious** in Appalachia. They have won protection for several endangered species.

10.

realm →

The Appalachians are a **realm** for wildlife. Bears and bobcats are the rulers of this animal kingdom.

EXERCISE 2   *Context Clues* ✍

Directions. Scan the definitions in Column A. Then, think about how the boldface words are used in the sentences in Column B. To complete the exercise, match each definition in Column A with the correct Vocabulary Word from Column B. Write the letter of your choice on the line provided. Finally, write the Vocabulary Word on the line before the definition.

COLUMN A	COLUMN B
____ **11.** word: _____: *n.* a person who designs plans for the construction of buildings or other structures	(A) Out in the woods, the main character in *Where the Red Fern Grows* felt like a king ruling his own small **realm**.
____ **12.** word: _____: *adj.* in a state resulting from a loss of hope; having a great need	(B) The boy's grandfather in *Where the Red Fern Grows* would never **betray** his grandson. He always tells the boy the truth.
____ **13.** word: _____: *v.* to glance at; to see briefly; *n.* a brief, quick view	(C) The red fern grew on the hounds' grave. It was an **eternal** symbol of love that would last forever.
____ **14.** word: _____: *n.* something offered to the gods; something given up for something of greater value; *v.* to offer something; to give up something of value for something else	(D) Most **architects** in Appalachia live in the cities, where they can find work designing buildings.
____ **15.** word: _____: *v.* to deceive; to turn against someone	(E) Some people who live in Appalachia give up high salaries to move there. They are willing to make this **sacrifice** to live in such a beautiful place.
____ **16.** word: _____: *adj.* existing forever; everlasting	(F) Some Appalachian school **districts** are very large in area but small in population. Such area divisions can make it difficult for families with school-age children to get the children to school.
____ **17.** word: _____: *n.* a person who is injured; one who suffers from some loss	(G) Poverty is a serious problem in parts of Appalachia. Many people are **desperate** in their need for food and medical care.
____ **18.** word: _____: *n.* a kingdom; an area	(H) In some parts of Appalachia, birds and animals, **victims** of development, have lost much of their home territory.
____ **19.** word: _____: *n.* a defined area or region; a geographical or political division	(I) If you look carefully, you can sometimes **glimpse** a deer as it leaps swiftly through the woods.
____ **20.** word: _____: *adj.* having gained a victory; winning	(J) **Victorious** hikers celebrate the achievement of their goal when they reach the end of the Appalachian Trail.

EXERCISE 3 Like Meanings and Opposite Meanings ✍

Directions. For each item below, circle the letter of the choice that means the same, or about the same, as the boldface word.

21. the best **architect**
- (A) high school teacher
- (B) building designer
- (C) shipbuilder
- (D) coal miner

22. a **district** of West Virginia
- (A) region
- (B) writer
- (C) school
- (D) trail

23. a mountain **realm**
- (A) lion
- (B) stream
- (C) path
- (D) area

24. a **sacrifice** for love
- (A) proof
- (B) offering
- (C) prayer
- (D) hope

25. the **victim** of a fierce attack
- (A) injured person
- (B) mugger
- (C) eyewitness
- (D) root cause

Directions. For each item below, circle the letter of the choice that means the opposite, or about the opposite, of the boldface word.

26. to **betray** a friend
- (A) support
- (B) hurt
- (C) describe
- (D) deceive

27. a **desperate** feeling
- (A) sad
- (B) hopeful
- (C) confused
- (D) angry

28. an **eternal** flame
- (A) temporary
- (B) enormous
- (C) everlasting
- (D) warm

29. to **glimpse** a cougar
- (A) run from
- (B) fear
- (C) stare at
- (D) shoot

30. a **victorious** group of people
- (A) losing
- (B) large
- (C) committed
- (D) bold

MAKING NEW WORDS YOUR OWN

Lesson 15 **CONTEXT: People and Places**

From Tipis to Igloos: How American Indians Adapted to the Land

When you think of traditional American Indian homes, what image comes to mind? Housing styles depended somewhat on climate and the raw materials available. Tradition and patterns of use were other factors that went into the design of American Indian houses. The Plains Indians, for example, moved often, so they built portable houses.

In the following exercises, you will have the opportunity to expand your vocabulary by reading about the traditional houses American Indians have made. Below are ten Vocabulary Words that will be used in these exercises.

abundant	descriptive	establish	possess	survey
barrier	desirable	flourish	prehistoric	terrain

EXERCISE 1 *Wordbusting*

Directions. Follow these instructions for this word and the nine words on the next page.
- Figure out the word's meaning by looking at its **context,** its **structure,** and its **sound.** Fill in at least one of the three **CSS** boxes. Alternate which boxes you complete.
- Then, look up the word in a dictionary, read all of its meanings, and write the meaning of the word as it is used in the sentence.
- Follow this same process for each of the Vocabulary Words on the next page. You will need to draw your own map for each word. Use a separate sheet of paper.

1.

abundant → Igloos are domed houses built from blocks of snow. Although snow is **abundant** in the Arctic, only certain kinds of snow can be used to make igloos.

Context:

Structure:

Sound:

Dictionary:

2.

barrier → The Plains peoples also took advantage of snow as a building material. In the winter, they would bank snow around the bases of their tipis as a **barrier** against wind.

3.

desirable → Igloos can be made only in the winter when snow is plentiful. On the other hand, tipis made **desirable** houses all year long. They could be lined for warmth in winter or opened up to the fresh air in summer.

4.

descriptive → To make tipis, tightly stitched buffalo hides were stretched over long poles. In one **descriptive** passage, a Spanish explorer gives a detailed account of a heavy rainstorm. He noted that no rain passed through the buffalo skin.

5.

establish → The Pueblo peoples built their homes from stone, wood, and adobe. When a Pueblo woman married, her husband would **establish** a home for them by building a new room onto her family's house.

6.

flourish → The Pueblos of the Southwest seem to do everything with a **flourish**. They built large, apartment-house villages and made beautiful pottery and woven cloth.

7.

possess → Some Pueblo villages were built on high mesas. These towns **possess** breathtaking views of the surrounding mountains and valleys.

8.

prehistoric → Scientists believe that the Pueblo peoples are distant relatives of the **prehistoric** Anasazi. No written records exist to tell us about the Anasazi.

9.

survey → Scientists **survey** Anasazi ruins and compare them with modern Pueblo structures. Through this kind of careful examination, they are able to draw conclusions about how the Anasazi might have lived.

10.

terrain → Anasazi ruins blend smoothly into the **terrain** of the desert Southwest. These American Indian houses often look like part of the land, like the canyon walls on which they are built.

EXERCISE 2 Context Clues

Directions. Scan the definitions in Column A. Then, think about how the boldface words are used in the sentences in Column B. To complete the exercise, match each definition in Column A with the correct Vocabulary Word from Column B. Write the letter of your choice on the line provided. Finally, write the Vocabulary Word on the line before the definition.

COLUMN A	COLUMN B

COLUMN A

_____ **11.** word: _____:
adj. concerned with describing; presented in detail

_____ **12.** word: _____:
v. to thrive; to succeed; to wave about; *n.* anything done in a showy way

_____ **13.** word: _____:
n. the ground or a piece of ground; a piece of ground for some use

_____ **14.** word: _____:
adj. plentiful; more than enough

_____ **15.** word: _____:
v. to set up; to bring about; to prove

_____ **16.** word: _____:
n. a detailed study; *v.* to inspect or review in detail; to view or consider

_____ **17.** word: _____:
v. to have something; to have as an attribute or quality

_____ **18.** word: _____:
n. something that prevents passage; a blockade; anything that separates

_____ **19.** word: _____:
adj. before recorded history

_____ **20.** word: _____:
adj. worth wanting or having; worthwhile; pleasing, attractive

COLUMN B

(A) Meghan is a sixth-grader who needs information to **establish** her own theory on American Indian homes.

(B) Meghan's theory is that the **abundant** water in one area or the lack of water in another area affected American Indian house styles.

(C) In the American Southwest, where water is scarce, American Indians were able to **flourish**. They adapted their lives to the climate and were able to do well.

(D) In the library, Meghan finds a detailed, **descriptive** article about the Pueblos.

(E) Meghan learns that the Pueblos live in the Southwest. For centuries, they built attractive houses from earth, stone, water, and wood. Many are still **desirable** dwellings.

(F) Meghan reads that the building styles of the Pueblos are divided into two types. The eastern Pueblos live near the Rio Grande. The western Pueblos live on drier **terrain** in New Mexico and Arizona.

(G) The lack of ground water is not much of a **barrier** to the western Pueblos. They are able to overcome the shortage by collecting rainwater.

(H) Meghan now **possesses** considerable information about the two different building methods. The western Pueblos, for example, use more stone and less water in building.

(I) The article also discusses the Anasazi, the Pueblos' **prehistoric** ancestors. Meghan would like to study these ancient people.

(J) Meghan's well-researched **survey** supports her theory. She is happy with her study of different types of dwellings.

EXERCISE 3   *Like Meanings and Opposite Meanings* ✍

Directions. For each item below, circle the letter of the choice that means the same, or about the same, as the boldface word.

21. moving with a **flourish**
- (A) jerking motion
- (B) stilted movement
- (C) wide sweep
- (D) waving about

22. Meghan's **descriptive** essay
- (A) boring
- (B) detailed
- (C) exciting
- (D) dangerous

23. a **prehistoric** ax
- (A) before recorded history
- (B) before the American Revolution
- (C) after written language
- (D) after recorded history

24. a published **survey**
- (A) a traditional law
- (B) a book about the ocean
- (C) a report on a broad area
- (D) a long, historical poem

25. rugged **terrain**
- (A) a small cave
- (B) waterfalls
- (C) a state highway
- (D) an area of ground

Directions. For each item below, circle the letter of the choice that means the opposite, or about the opposite, of the boldface word.

26. **abundant** snow
- (A) old
- (B) available
- (C) scarce
- (D) useful

27. to **possess** sturdy houses
- (A) lack
- (B) build
- (C) decorate
- (D) own

28. a high **barrier**
- (A) collar
- (B) opening
- (C) wall
- (D) maintain

29. to **establish** a cultural center
- (A) organize
- (B) make happen
- (C) govern
- (D) bring to an end

30. **desirable** housing
- (A) unwanted
- (B) interesting
- (C) practical
- (D) sturdy

MAKING NEW WORDS YOUR OWN

Lesson 16   **CONTEXT:** People and Places

Kipling's Just So Stories: *Myths of Nature*

In *Just So Stories*, Rudyard Kipling (1865–1936) creates myths of the world's beginnings. These stories explain how the camel got his hump, why the elephant's trunk is so long, and how the leopard got its spots. Kipling lived and traveled in India in the late 1890s. Some of his other books are *The Jungle Book, Captains Courageous*, and *Kim*. The *Just So Stories* are some of his best-loved tales.

In the following exercises, you will have the opportunity to expand your vocabulary by reading about Kipling's *Just So Stories*. These ten Vocabulary Words will be used.

dramatic	feat	irregular	marvel	satisfy
extraordinary	inaccurate	leisure	numerous	vicinity

EXERCISE 1   *Wordbusting*

Directions.   Follow these instructions for this word and the nine words on the next page.
- Figure out the word's meaning by looking at its **context,** its **structure,** and its **sound.** Fill in at least one of the three **CSS** boxes. Alternate which boxes you complete.
- Then, look up the word in a dictionary, read all of its meanings, and write the meaning of the word as it is used in the sentence.
- Follow this same process for each of the Vocabulary Words on the next page. You will need to draw your own map for each word. Use a separate sheet of paper.

1.

(dramatic) → In "How the Whale Got His Throat," a mariner makes a whale very uncomfortable by jumping up and down. The mariner used **dramatic** gestures, as if he were on stage.

Context:

Structure:

Sound:

Dictionary:

2.

(**satisfy**) ➤ Kipling's whale cannot **satisfy** his hunger even though he eats all but one fish in the sea.

3.

(**extraordinary**) ➤ Early readers of Kipling found his stories **extraordinary.** They had never read such amazing tales.

4.

(**feat**) ➤ In "The Beginning of the Armadillos," the hedgehog learns how to swim—an unusual **feat**. His remarkable act allows him to escape from a jaguar.

5.

(**inaccurate**) ➤ Kipling's story "How the Camel Got His Hump," is **inaccurate,** but these tales do not attempt to be factual.

6.

(**irregular**) ➤ A man gives the leopard spots by pressing his fingers against the fur. The spots are not **irregular** but are spaced evenly in groups of five.

7.

(**leisure**) ➤ In "The Cat That Walked by Himself," the cat gains the right to live a life of **leisure**. Because a woman is grateful to him, he is fed without having to do any work.

8.

(**marvel**) ➤ When the elephant's child returns from visiting the crocodile, his family is surprised by his appearance. They think his wonderful new trunk is a **marvel**.

9.

(**numerous**) ➤ A Parsee places **numerous** cake crumbs inside a rhinoceros' skin. There are so many crumbs that the rhinoceros is very uncomfortable and itchy.

10.

(**vicinity**) ➤ The hedgehog and tortoise live in the **vicinity** of the Amazon River. In this area, they find lots of food to eat.

EXERCISE 2 | *Context Clues* ✍️

Directions. Scan the definitions in Column A. Then, think about how the boldface words are used in the sentences in Column B. To complete the exercise, match each definition in Column A with the correct Vocabulary Word from Column B. Write the letter of your choice on the line provided. Finally, write the Vocabulary Word on the line before the definition.

COLUMN A

_____ **11.** word: _____:
adj. pertaining to drama or theater; having the forced qualities of a drama; striking

_____ **12.** word: _____:
n. something that is wonderful or surprising; *v.* to be amazed at something

_____ **13.** word: _____:
adj. not straight; uneven; not following established rule or method

_____ **14.** word: _____:
v. to fill the needs or requirements of; to free from doubt

_____ **15.** word: _____:
n. free and unoccupied time; spare time; freedom from work

_____ **16.** word: _____:
adj. very many; consisting of many people or things

_____ **17.** word: _____:
n. a remarkable deed or accomplishment

_____ **18.** word: _____:
n. the state of being close by; the area surrounding a particular place; the neighborhood of a place

_____ **19.** word: _____:
adj. markedly different from the usual; amazing; exceptional

_____ **20.** word: _____:
adj. not correct; not exact

COLUMN B

(A) No one should call Kipling's *Just So Stories* **inaccurate** accounts. Their purpose is to entertain and amuse.

(B) In "The Butterfly That Stamped," a very **dramatic,** striking thing occurs when the butterfly stamps his foot: The palace disappears!

(C) In "Old Man Kangaroo," the kangaroo is amazed. He **marvels** at the change in himself.

(D) In "The Cat That Walked by Himself," the dog, horse, and cow all stay nearby, in the **vicinity** of the cave.

(E) The mariner accomplishes a remarkable **feat** in "How the Whale Got His Throat." He uses his suspenders to tie a set of bars in the whale's throat.

(F) The jaguar is confused by the tortoise and the hedgehog. He is never **satisfied,** or fully sure, about which is which.

(G) The jaguar is also confused when the hedgehog and tortoise act in an **irregular** way. They do not follow the rules that the jaguar's mother had set out for him.

(H) In "Old Man Kangaroo," the kangaroo has no **leisure** when he is being chased by the dingo. There is simply no time to rest.

(I) When the leopard enters the forest, he thinks the other animals look **extraordinary**. Each is different from the others.

(J) The elephant child is curious about many things. They are too **numerous** to list.

EXERCISE 3   *Like Meanings and Opposite Meanings* ✍

Directions. For each item below, circle the letter of the choice that means the same, or about the same, as the boldface word.

21. a **dramatic** appearance
- (A) ordinary
- (B) elegant
- (C) striking
- (D) meaningful

22. the **feat** of the camel
- (A) remarkable deed
- (B) hump
- (C) original owner
- (D) appearance

23. the **leisure** to read the stories
- (A) desire
- (B) free time
- (C) request
- (D) requirement

24. **inaccurate** information
- (A) truthful
- (B) unimportant
- (C) incorrect
- (D) unbiased

25. the **vicinity** of the river
- (A) banks
- (B) village
- (C) fish
- (D) neighborhood

Directions. For each item below, circle the letter of the choice that means the opposite, or about the opposite, of the boldface word.

26. an **extraordinary** elephant child
- (A) usual
- (B) young
- (C) annoying
- (D) odd

27. **irregular** spots
- (A) uneven
- (B) brown
- (C) evenly spaced
- (D) widely spaced

28. to **marvel** about rhinoceros skin
- (A) be curious
- (B) be bored
- (C) be amazed
- (D) be scared

29. **numerous** fishes
- (A) few
- (B) a dozen
- (C) twenty
- (D) very many

30. to **satisfy** the elephant child's curiosity
- (A) frighten away
- (B) laugh at
- (C) decrease
- (D) be shocked by

MAKING NEW WORDS YOUR OWN

Lesson 17 | **CONTEXT:** People and Places

The Vikings: Adventuring to North America

History books used to teach that Columbus was the first European to reach North America. A recent discovery, however, indicates that the Vikings reached North America five hundred years before Columbus. Anne Stine, an archaeologist, discovered the remains of a Viking encampment in northern Newfoundland. Many scientists today believe that the Vikings did not stop only in Newfoundland but traveled as far south as Massachusetts or New York.

In the following exercises, you will have the opportunity to expand your vocabulary by reading about the Vikings in North America. These ten Vocabulary Words will be used.

ambitious	exclaim	honorable	portrait	wardrobe
envy	heir	oath	reign	yacht

EXERCISE 1 *Wordbusting*

Directions. Follow these instructions for this word and the nine words on the next page.
- Figure out the word's meaning by looking at its **context,** its **structure,** and its **sound.** Fill in at least one of the three **CSS** boxes. Alternate which boxes you complete.
- Then, look up the word in a dictionary, read all of its meanings, and write the meaning of the word as it is used in the sentence.
- Follow this same process for each of the Vocabulary Words on the next page. You will need to draw your own map for each word. Use a separate sheet of paper.

1.

(ambitious) ➡️ The people who lived in Scandinavia from the ninth to the twelfth centuries were known as Vikings. **Ambitious** young Viking men, that is, those who wanted to get ahead, traveled to find fortune.

Context:	Structure:	Sound:

Dictionary:

2.

envy → At that time, Scandinavia was not as rich as the rest of Europe, partly because the soil there was not as good for farming as that in France and England. For this reason, the Vikings may have **envied** their richer neighbors.

3.

exclaim → The Vikings raided the countries to the south. Although the people of England and France **exclaimed** loudly, no one answered their cries for help, and the raids continued.

4.

oath → The Vikings were feared and hated throughout Europe for their warlike behavior and their cursing. They are famous for their violent actions and loud **oaths**.

5.

wardrobe → An important part of a Viking's **wardrobe** was his suit of armor, made of thick animal hides. His clothing also included a long, heavy shirt, leather shoes, and a leather helmet.

6.

yacht → Viking ships were light and fast. Still, they were very different in design from today's **yachts,** which are used for pleasure cruises or racing. Viking ships carried horses, cows, pigs, and warriors on long, difficult journeys.

7.

heir → The Vikings colonized new territory. The Viking Naddod laid claim to Iceland. His great-grandnephew, Erik the Red, was the **heir** to this family tradition of colonization. He colonized Greenland.

8.

reign → Most Norse legends are about the deeds of a king and the events that happened during the period of his **reign**.

9.

honorable → Old Norse sagas, or legends, depict the warriors as **honorable** men. These stories indicate that Erik the Red and his son, Leif Eriksson, were respected by the Viking people.

10.

portrait → From the Norse legend *Erik's Saga,* we can piece together a **portrait** of Erik the Red. The picture that emerges is of a clever, brave, and confident man.

EXERCISE 2 Context Clues ✍

Directions. Scan the definitions in Column A. Then, think about how the boldface words are used in the sentences in Column B. To complete the exercise, match each definition in Column A with the correct Vocabulary Word from Column B. Write the letter of your choice on the line provided. Finally, write the Vocabulary Word on the line before the definition.

COLUMN A	COLUMN B
_____ **11.** word: _____: *n.* a person who inherits another's property or traits	(A) Long ago, the Vikings **reigned** over the huge northern island of Greenland. The Vikings also ruled Iceland.
_____ **12.** word: _____: *n.* dislike or uneasiness because of another person's possessions or advantages; *v.* to be jealous of	(B) The settlement of Greenland—a harsh place with long, cold, dark winters—was an **ambitious** project. It took much effort to carry out.
_____ **13.** word: _____: *n.* a drawing, painting, sculpture, photograph, or description of someone	(C) Eventually the settlement was abandoned because no new people came to the colony, and the settlers left no **heirs** to receive their holdings.
_____ **14.** word: _____: *n.* one's collection of clothes; a closet, cupboard, or room for clothes	(D) Because life was hard in Greenland, the Greenlanders might have **envied** people who lived in warmer places.
_____ **15.** word: _____: *adj.* greatly desirous of something; eager; demanding great effort or skill	(E) A piece of carved ivory that looks like a **portrait** of a Viking was discovered in an old Eskimo camp. This likeness is evidence that the Vikings had contact with the Eskimos.
_____ **16.** word: _____: *v.* to cry out; to speak suddenly in surprise or anger	(F) Until recently, there was no proof that the Vikings had traveled south along the Canadian coast. Then, one woman promised to carry out her dream. She made an **oath** to discover the truth about the Vikings.
_____ **17.** word: _____: *n.* a formal declaration of honesty or loyalty; a swear word; a curse	(G) This woman was Anne Stine, an archaeologist. One summer she sailed a **yacht** down Canada's coast.
_____ **18.** word: _____: *n.* a small boat for pleasure or racing	(H) You can imagine how Stine must have **exclaimed** when she discovered the ruins of a Viking village in Newfoundland.
_____ **19.** word: _____: *n.* a power or rule over; a period of rule; *v.* to rule or have power over	(I) Stine made a careful study of the ruins. There were no signs of the clothing that made up the Vikings' **wardrobes;** the cloth had rotted.
_____ **20.** word: _____: *adj.* worthy of being honored or respected; having a sense of right and wrong	(J) In their own way, Viking warriors were **honorable** men. They had their own concept of right and wrong. Right was bravery, and wrong was giving up without a fight.

EXERCISE 3 *Like Meanings and Opposite Meanings* ✍

Directions. For each item below, circle the letter of the choice that means the same, or about the same, as the boldface word.

21. a solemn **oath**
   (A) decision
   (B) lecture
   (C) comment
   (D) declaration

22. an empty **wardrobe**
   (A) closet for clothes
   (B) large glass bottle
   (C) small ship
   (D) suitcase

23. the **heir** to a fortune
   (A) child
   (B) inheritor
   (C) judge
   (D) lawyer

24. a life-size **portrait**
   (A) young tree
   (B) full-length mirror
   (C) picture of someone
   (D) suit of armor

25. a private **yacht**
   (A) car
   (B) beach
   (C) meadow
   (D) boat

Directions. For each item below, circle the letter of the choice that means the opposite, or about the opposite, of the boldface word.

26. the **ambitious** Viking
   (A) halfhearted
   (B) violent
   (C) athletic
   (D) eager

27. a feeling of **envy**
   (A) jealousy
   (B) sympathy
   (C) pride
   (D) desire

28. to **exclaim** with anger
   (A) whisper
   (B) scream
   (C) threaten
   (D) explain

29. to **reign** justly
   (A) organize
   (B) dominate
   (C) abuse
   (D) serve

30. an **honorable** leader
   (A) worthy of respect
   (B) honest
   (C) not respectable
   (D) conquering

MAKING NEW WORDS YOUR OWN

Lesson 18 **CONTEXT:** People and Places

Desert Mysteries: Prehistoric Civilizations

Until about seven thousand years ago, our ancestors did not know how to grow food. The Cochise people, American Indians of Mexico and the Southwestern United States, were the first people to grow corn. Through the work of archaeologists, people who study the things that ancient peoples have left behind, we have learned about how the Cochise lived. Their artifacts include pottery, houses, and ancient garbage dumps.

In the following exercises, you will have the opportunity to expand your vocabulary by reading about the ancient civilizations of the Southwest. Below are ten Vocabulary Words that will be used in these exercises.

arid	investment	luxurious	relate	solitary
counterfeit	knapsack	ornamental	request	transparent

EXERCISE 1 *Wordbusting*

Directions. Follow these instructions for this word and the nine words on the next page.
- Figure out the word's meaning by looking at its **context,** its **structure,** and its **sound.** Fill in at least one of the three **CSS** boxes. Alternate which boxes you complete.
- Then, look up the word in a dictionary, read all of its meanings, and write the meaning of the word as it is used in the sentence.
- Follow this same process for each of the Vocabulary Words on the next page. You will need to draw your own map for each word. Use a separate sheet of paper.

1.

arid → The Southwest is a primarily **arid** region. To grow there, plants must be able to survive with little rainfall.

Context:

Structure:

Sound:

Dictionary:

Name _____ Date _____ Class _____

2.

(investment) ➤ The Hohokam were the descendants of the ancient Cochise. The Hohokam lived near rivers in southern Arizona. They made a huge **investment** of time and energy to create irrigation canals.

3.

(knapsack) ➤ On a hike out to the ruins of the Hohokam city, you will need to carry water in a **knapsack**. Once, Hohokam canals flowed into the city. Now, the only water around is what you carry on your back.

4.

(luxurious) ➤ The Hohokam ruins are near present-day Phoenix, Arizona. Life in this ancient city was comfortable, even **luxurious**. Harvests were rich, so some people probably had time to relax.

5.

(ornamental) ➤ Archaeologists have discovered decorative, **ornamental** jewelry and crafts made by the Hohokam.

6.

(relate) ➤ Scientists **relate** these decorative objects to the lifestyle of the people who made them. Because these objects would have taken time to make, scientists believe that the Hohokam must have had a lot of spare time.

7.

(counterfeit) ➤ Many people are eager to own ancient carvings and pottery. For this reason, some dishonest people make **counterfeit** artifacts.

8.

(request) ➤ If you ask for information on the religious beliefs of the Hohokam, your **request** cannot be granted easily. Some archaeologists believe that the large, thick-walled Hohokam ruins were once temples. Others think they might have been forts.

9.

(solitary) ➤ Imagine that you stand at the foot of one of these **solitary** buildings. You are struck by the loneliness of the place. Who built this massive structure with its five-foot-thick adobe walls? Where did these people go?

10.

(transparent) ➤ The answer to this question is far from **transparent**. No one knows what happened to the great Hohokam civilization. By the time the Spanish arrived, the Hohokam cities had been abandoned.

EXERCISE 2 *Context Clues*

Directions. Scan the definitions in Column A. Then, think about how the boldface words are used in the sentences in Column B. To complete the exercise, match each definition in Column A with the correct Vocabulary Word from Column B. Write the letter of your choice on the line provided. Finally, write the Vocabulary Word on the line before the definition.

COLUMN A	COLUMN B

COLUMN A

_____ **11.** word: _____:
n. an imitation intended to deceive; *v.* to make an imitation in order to deceive; *adj.* made in imitation of something

_____ **12.** word: _____:
n. the act of asking for something; something asked for; *v.* to ask for

_____ **13.** word: _____:
n. a bag or case worn on the back

_____ **14.** word: _____:
adj. decorative

_____ **15.** word: _____:
adj. living or being alone; without others; single; only; lonely, empty

_____ **16.** word: _____:
n. something purchased for future profit; effort spent with the expectation of return

_____ **17.** word: _____:
adj. fond of or enjoying luxury; splendid; rich; comfortable; expensive

_____ **18.** word: _____:
adj. capable of being seen through; easily understood; very clear

_____ **19.** word: _____:
v. to tell the story of; to connect or associate; to have some connection to

_____ **20.** word: _____:
adj. not enough rainfall; not interesting; not fertile

COLUMN B

(A) Randy is interested in ancient Anasazi people who once lived in the Southwest. He decides to take a camping trip to that area. He packs a tent and clothes into his **knapsack**.

(B) He visits the Anasazi cliff dwellings at Mesa Verde National Park. It will be hard to **relate** to his family the drama of these ancient houses. A snapshot will not tell the whole story.

(C) After lunch, Randy decides to take a hike along the Petroglyph Trail. The trail is **solitary**. Randy doesn't meet anyone.

(D) The trail leads to a large stone panel with markings cut into it. These markings are called *petroglyphs*. Randy wonders if the markings have meaning or if they are only **ornamental**.

(E) At the park museum, Randy asks a favor. He **requests** that a park ranger explain the petroglyphs to him.

(F) She tells Randy, "Archaeologists have made a great **investment** of time to answer that question. So far, their efforts have not paid off."

(G) In the museum, Randy sees a large display of ancient Anasazi baskets. The collection demonstrates that the Anasazi led productive lives, not **arid** ones.

(H) He wonders how the fragile baskets could have survived. The ranger assures him that they are not **counterfeit**. They are the real thing.

(I) Randy camps in the Mesa Verde campground. His tent is not **luxurious**. However, he feels that the splendor of nearby Anasazi Cliff Palace is better than any four-star hotel.

(J) Through the **transparent** plastic of his tent window, he sees the same stars the Anasazi saw.

EXERCISE 3 *Like Meanings and Opposite Meanings* ✍

Directions. For each item below, circle the letter of the choice that means the same, or about the same, as the boldface word.

21. the **arid** region
(A) productive
(B) infertile
(C) distant
(D) sandy

22. a financial **investment**
(A) something bought for future profit
(B) a business expense
(C) a salary
(D) a person who buys stocks and bonds

23. to carry my **knapsack**
(A) folding chair
(B) lantern
(C) backpack
(D) hammer

24. to **request** a favorite song
(A) offer
(B) open
(C) discard something
(D) ask for something

25. to **relate** a myth
(A) remember
(B) repeat often
(C) tell
(D) shout happily

Directions. For each item below, circle the letter of the choice that means the opposite, or about the opposite, of the boldface word.

26. a **counterfeit** artifact
(A) broken
(B) genuine
(C) ancient
(D) worthless

27. designed to be **ornamental**
(A) useful
(B) cheap
(C) expensive
(D) pleasing

28. a **solitary** example
(A) bland
(B) excellent
(C) multiple
(D) important

29. the **transparent** lake
(A) easily reached
(B) deep
(C) very clouded
(D) inviting

30. the **luxurious** temple
(A) large
(B) restored
(C) foreign
(D) plain

MAKING NEW WORDS YOUR OWN

Lesson 19 CONTEXT: People and Places

Haystacks and Waterlilies: Impressions of Monet

French painter Claude Monet (1840–1926) led a movement called *Impressionism*. He painted his personal response to—his impression of—natural and human-made objects. At first, Monet and other Impressionist painters were not accepted by the public, but eventually people came to appreciate Impressionist art. Monet moved from Paris to an estate at Giverny where he painted his famous pictures of gardens and waterlilies.

In the following exercises, you will have the opportunity to expand your vocabulary by reading about Claude Monet. These ten Vocabulary Words will be used.

appropriate	contribute	gorgeous	inviting	ordinarily
assume	cultivate	hearty	occasion	quantity

EXERCISE 1 *Wordbusting*

Directions. Follow these instructions for this word and the nine words on the next page.
- Figure out the word's meaning by looking at its **context,** its **structure,** and its **sound.** Fill in at least one of the three **CSS** boxes. Alternate which boxes you complete.
- Then, look up the word in a dictionary, read all of its meanings, and write the meaning of the word as it is used in the sentence.
- Follow this same process for each of the Vocabulary Words on the next page. You will need to draw your own map for each word. Use a separate sheet of paper.

1.

(**appropriate**) ⟶ At an exhibit in 1874, Monet showed a painting called *Impression: Sunrise.* An art critic ridiculed the exhibit by using the term "impressionism." These artists then **appropriated** the term, using it to describe their work.

Context:	Structure:	Sound:

Dictionary:

2.

assume ➔ Monet is very popular today. However, do not **assume,** or accept as true, that he was popular during his lifetime unless you study the facts.

3.

contribute ➔ Monet **contributed** greatly to the world of art. He gave other artists a new way of looking at light and nature.

4.

ordinarily ➔ When he moved to the country, Monet's life fell into a pattern. He **ordinarily** woke up around four or five in the morning to see what the weather was like.

5.

cultivate ➔ At Giverny, Monet was able to **cultivate** a beautiful garden. He loved to grow plants.

6.

gorgeous ➔ The Art Institute of Chicago has several of Monet's most **gorgeous** paintings of waterlilies. I have never seen anything more magnificent!

7.

inviting ➔ Some of Monet's paintings are especially **inviting**. Looking at the waterlilies, for instance, you almost feel tempted to walk into the water.

8.

hearty ➔ Monet had a **hearty** relationship with his friends; he was warm and friendly with them.

9.

occasion ➔ For Monet, as for most artists, every sale of a painting was an **occasion,** a special cause for celebration.

10.

quantity ➔ Monet was his own harshest critic and destroyed hundreds of pictures. Fortunately, a large **quantity** of paintings still remain for our pleasure today.

EXERCISE 2 *Context Clues* ✍

Directions. Scan the definitions in Column A. Then, think about how the boldface words are used in the sentences in Column B. To complete the exercise, match each definition in Column A with the correct Vocabulary Word from Column B. Write the letter of your choice on the line provided. Finally, write the Vocabulary Word on the line before the definition.

COLUMN A	COLUMN B

COLUMN A

_____ **11.** word: _____:
adj. right for the purpose; suitable; proper; *v.* to take for one's own or exclusive use

_____ **12.** word: _____:
adj. very warm and friendly; enthusiastic; satisfying and plentiful; strong and healthy

_____ **13.** word: _____:
n. a favorable time; an opportunity; a special time or event for celebration

_____ **14.** word: _____:
v. to take upon oneself; to undertake; to put on; to suppose something to be a fact; to take for granted

_____ **15.** word: _____:
adj. magnificent; splendid; beautiful

_____ **16.** word: _____:
adv. usually; in a normal manner

_____ **17.** word: _____:
n. an amount; a portion

_____ **18.** word: _____:
v. to prepare and use land for growing crops; to grow plants, crops; to improve or develop

_____ **19.** word: _____:
adj. tempting; attractive; enticing

_____ **20.** word: _____:
v. to give to a common fund or cause; to assist in bringing something about

COLUMN B

(A) Another school of painting in fashion about the same time as Impressionism was Realism. Realist artists **ordinarily** tried to make their paintings look exactly like their subjects.

(B) Sometimes it takes time to develop a liking for a certain style of painting. Have you **cultivated** an appreciation of Impressionism, or do you prefer Realist painting?

(C) Monet's early critics did not think his paintings were **appropriate**. They felt the Impressionists made improper use of their subjects.

(D) Public approval of Impressionism **contributed** to Monet's success. This approval helped bring about acceptance by art critics.

(E) Monet became a successful artist and was able to buy a country estate with a certain amount, or **quantity,** of his income.

(F) At Giverny, Monet built a **gorgeous** bridge in the waterlily garden. He painted this beautiful bridge many times.

(G) Generally, Monet was not attracted by images of the city. He found nature a more **inviting** subject.

(H) Living in the country gave Monet an appetite. He ate a **hearty,** satisfying breakfast every morning before setting about his work.

(I) Monet loved to take trips. Any event away from his home became an **occasion** for travel.

(J) Monet **assumed** the responsibility for his large family. His success made it possible for him to support them well.

EXERCISE 3 *Like Meanings and Opposite Meanings* ✍

Directions. For each item below, circle the letter of the choice that means the same, or about the same, as the boldface word.

21. to **assume** a big project
(A) work on
(B) undertake
(C) ask about
(D) finish

22. an **occasion** for a celebration
(A) costume
(B) poor reason
(C) opportunity
(D) ordinary time

23. to **cultivate** relationships with other artists
(A) develop
(B) end
(C) watch
(D) ruin

24. a **hearty** approach to life
(A) cautious
(B) unhappy
(C) uninteresting
(D) enthusiastic

25. a **quantity** of paint
(A) splash
(B) amount
(C) gallon
(D) cup

Directions. For each item below, circle the letter of the choice that means the opposite, or about the opposite, of the boldface word.

26. an **appropriate** question
(A) suitable
(B) obvious
(C) improper
(D) interesting

27. the **gorgeous** waterlilies
(A) very beautiful
(B) faded and wilted
(C) underwater
(D) yellowish

28. an **inviting** story
(A) unappealing
(B) long
(C) brief
(D) familiar

29. to **contribute** a small amount
(A) find
(B) give
(C) take away
(D) ask for

30. **ordinarily** pleasant
(A) with enthusiasm
(B) unusually
(C) daily
(D) usually

MAKING NEW WORDS YOUR OWN

Lesson 20 | CONTEXT: People and Places

Island Hopping in the Caribbean

The Caribbean islands—Jamaica, Cuba, and Puerto Rico are the largest—are famous for colorful fish and coral and for rare tropical birds. Because the islands are separated from one another by water, each island has its own culture, history, and languages. People speak Spanish in Puerto Rico and Cuba, but French is spoken in Haiti. On the island of Aruba, people speak a language called Papiamento.

In the following exercises, you will have the opportunity to expand your vocabulary by reading about the Caribbean islands. These ten Vocabulary Words will be used.

| boast | disadvantage | exert | import | precipitation |
| contrast | eliminate | export | luscious | tradition |

EXERCISE 1   Wordbusting ✍️

Directions. Follow these instructions for this word and the nine words on the next page.
- Figure out the word's meaning by looking at its **context,** its **structure,** and its **sound.** Fill in at least one of the three **CSS** boxes. Alternate which boxes you complete.
- Then, look up the word in a dictionary, read all of its meanings, and write the meaning of the word as it is used in the sentence.
- Follow this same process for each of the Vocabulary Words on the next page. You will need to draw your own map for each word. Use a separate sheet of paper.

1.

(boast) ➝ Carnival takes place on the island of Trinidad from late February to early March. Trinidadians **boast** about their Carnival, proudly claiming that it is the best celebration in the world.

Context:

Structure:

Sound:

Dictionary:

Name _____ Date _____ Class _____

2.

(contrast) ➔ The lush vegetation of Trinidad forms a **contrast** to the dry, rocky landscape of Aruba. These islands, seven hundred miles apart, are very different.

3.

(disadvantage) ➔ One **disadvantage** of Aruba's dry climate is that there is very little fresh water on the island.

4.

(eliminate) ➔ The St. Vincent parrot is a rare bird that lives only on the island of St. Vincent. This species is in danger of extinction because the destruction of island forests threatens to **eliminate** the parrot's natural habitat.

5.

(exert) ➔ Seasonal storms **exert** themselves on the islands of the Caribbean. Every year, hurricanes blow in forcefully from the Atlantic and strike the islands.

6.

(export) ➔ Bananas, which are grown on many of the islands and sold all over the world, are a major Caribbean **export**.

7.

(import) ➔ There are not many farms on the island of St. Eustatius. People who live on St. Eustatius must **import** most of their food from other places.

8.

 (luscious) ➔ Spices such as cinnamon are grown in the Caribbean and used in the delicious local dishes. These dishes are so **luscious** that people all over the world enjoy them.

9.

(precipitation) ➔ On the beaches of Jamaica, the weather is almost always warm and clear. High in the Blue Mountains, however, there is much **precipitation** in the forms of both rain and snow.

10.

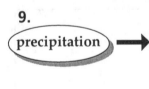 (tradition) ➔ Brightly painted houses are a Caribbean **tradition**. People have believed for a long time that bright, cheerful colors bring good luck.

EXERCISE 2 *Context Clues* 🖎

Directions. Scan the definitions in Column A. Then, think about how the boldface words are used in the sentences in Column B. To complete the exercise, match each definition in Column A with the correct Vocabulary Word from Column B. Write the letter of your choice on the line provided. Finally, write the Vocabulary Word on the line before the definition.

COLUMN A	COLUMN B

_____ **11.** word: _____:
v. to talk proudly about oneself; to brag

_____ **12.** word: _____:
v. to show differences between; *n.* a striking difference

_____ **13.** word: _____:
n. something brought in from another country or place; importance; *v.* to bring in goods from another country

_____ **14.** word: _____:
n. the handing down of stories, beliefs, or customs through generations; a custom

_____ **15.** word: _____:
n. a drawback; a handicap

_____ **16.** word: _____:
n. a bringing on suddenly; a sudden fall or rush; snow, rain, or sleet

_____ **17.** word: _____:
n. something sent to another place or country; *v.* to carry or send goods to another country for sale

_____ **18.** word: _____:
v. to put forth vigorously

_____ **19.** word: _____:
v. to take out, remove, get rid of

_____ **20.** word: _____:
adj. very pleasing to the tastes or smell; pleasing to the senses; lavishly adorned; excessively sweet

(A) The relaxed life style of my cousins in the Virgin Islands is such a **contrast** to the hustle and bustle of my life here in New York City.

(B) My brother ran into the water at St. Thomas Beach in such a hurry that he did not notice the water was full of jellyfish. As a result of his **precipitation,** he was badly stung.

(C) Our cousins told us an old story about Sir Francis Drake. According to **tradition,** the explorer used Magen Bay Beach as a lookout.

(D) No doubt Drake discovered how **luscious** the Caribbean is. He may have preferred the warm, colorful islands to life in England.

(E) My uncle Marcus told me that tourism is of great **import** in the Virgin Islands. The economies of the islands depend on tourism.

(F) While some islanders do not like the tourism, it will probably never be **eliminated** because it is so important to the islands' economy.

(G) Although it is tempting just to relax, travelers should **exert** themselves to see the real life of the islands.

(H) The island of Grand Cayman **boasts** a sea turtle farm. To check the truth of this claim, we went to see the farm.

(I) Sea turtle meat is not usually **exported** to other countries. Instead, it is sold to restaurants on the island.

(J) A girl I met speaks English, Dutch, and Papiamento. She was surprised that I speak only one language. I told her that in New York it is not a **disadvantage** to know only English.

EXERCISE 3 — *Like Meanings and Opposite Meanings*

Directions. For each item below, circle the letter of the choice that means the same, or about the same, as the boldface word.

21. to **boast** about a skill
  (A) worry
  (B) talk
  (C) brag
  (D) know

22. a Jamaican **tradition**
  (A) celebration
  (B) custom
  (C) culture
  (D) history

23. to **exert** influence
  (A) maintain
  (B) put forth
  (C) demand
  (D) give away

24. heavy **precipitation**
  (A) a surprise
  (B) rainfall
  (C) evaporation
  (D) pressure

25. to **export** bananas
  (A) send to another country
  (B) return to the farmers
  (C) eat a great deal of
  (D) use as a medicine

Directions. For each item below, circle the letter of the choice that means the opposite, or about the opposite, of the boldface word.

26. a strong **contrast**
  (A) difference
  (B) dislike
  (C) similarity
  (D) opinion

27. an unfortunate **disadvantage**
  (A) handicap
  (B) aid
  (C) disaster
  (D) inability

28. to **import** oil
  (A) send to another country
  (B) offer for sale
  (C) increase the price of
  (D) set on fire

29. the **luscious** peaches
  (A) rotten
  (B) forbidden
  (C) delicious
  (D) early

30. to **eliminate** a choice
  (A) keep
  (B) forget
  (C) think about
  (D) get rid of

MAKING NEW WORDS YOUR OWN

Lesson 21 | CONTEXT: Ecology and Environment
Down to the Sea with Jacques Cousteau

Jacques Cousteau (1910–1997), a French underwater explorer, became interested in the sea during his service in the French Navy. His friendship with two other sailors led to the three men working together for many years. They studied the shark and the whale, dove for sunken treasure, and explored a coral sea. What made these adventures possible was a ship named Calypso and the scuba tank that Cousteau and Emile Gagnan invented.

In the following exercises, you will have the opportunity to expand your vocabulary by reading about Cousteau's ship, *Calypso*. These ten Vocabulary Words will be used.

appreciate	entertain	inform	mammoth	theme
braille	genuine	inspiration	text	visual

EXERCISE 1 *Wordbusting* ✍

Directions. Follow these instructions for this word and the nine words on the next page.
- Figure out the word's meaning by looking at its **context,** its **structure,** and its **sound.** Fill in at least one of the three **CSS** boxes. Alternate which boxes you complete.
- Then, look up the word in a dictionary, read all of its meanings, and write the meaning of the word as it is used in the sentence.
- Follow this same process for each of the Vocabulary Words on the next page. You will need to draw your own map for each word. Use a separate sheet of paper.

1.

(appreciate) → The *Calypso* was an old United States minesweeper being used as a ferry after World War II. Cousteau learned to **appreciate** such a vessel. He understood the worth of a ship that could hold a crew of thirty people, a helicopter, and a hot-air balloon.

Context:	Structure:	Sound:

Dictionary:

2.

mammoth ➤ A 139-foot-long ship may seem **mammoth** to some. *Calypso* is small compared to many other ships, although it has two engines, a repair workshop, and walk-in refrigerators.

3.

braille ➤ Cousteau's adventures in the *Calypso* helped to open the sea to people much as the system of **braille** opened the world of books to the blind.

4.

inspiration ➤ Cousteau's work aboard *Calypso* is an **inspiration** to amateurs and scientists alike. He had a strong influence on others who wished to explore the sea.

5.

genuine ➤ Cousteau's team acquired a two-person exploration submarine. It had no propeller, and it could take divers to depths of 1150 feet—a chance for some **genuine** adventure.

6.

text ➤ In 1967, *Calypso* set out on a three-year expedition. During this trip, the first twelve films of the TV series, *The Undersea World of Jacques Cousteau,* were filmed. A **text,** or written work, about the sea may be interesting, but a film is especially gripping.

7.

entertain ➤ Cousteau **entertained** audiences with his award-winning movies about the sea. The films *The Silent World* and *World Without Sun* held the interest of thousands of viewers.

8.

inform ➤ The films made by the crew of *Calypso* have served to **inform** viewers about underwater life. Audiences learned about life forms they never knew existed.

9.

theme ➤ Cousteau has also written books about his adventures. The **theme,** or subject, of his work is the fascinating world beneath the sea. *Diving Companions,* for example, talks about two sea lions living aboard *Calypso.*

10.

visual ➤ The many photographs in Cousteau's books are a **visual** treat for the reader.

EXERCISE 2   Context Clues ✍

Directions. Scan the definitions in Column A. Then, think about how the boldface words are used in the sentences in Column B. To complete the exercise, match each definition in Column A with the correct Vocabulary Word from Column B. Write the letter of your choice on the line provided. Finally, write the Vocabulary Word on the line before the definition.

COLUMN A	COLUMN B

COLUMN A

_____ **11.** word: _____:
adj. connected with sight; having qualities that can be seen

_____ **12.** word: _____:
n. a topic, subject, or main idea of a written work, sermon, speech, and so on

_____ **13.** word: _____:
v. to give knowledge of something to; to tell someone something

_____ **14.** word: _____:
n. an inhaling; a strong influence; a stimulus to creativity

_____ **15.** word: _____:
n. a type of extinct elephant; *adj.* huge

_____ **16.** word: _____:
adj. real; true; authentic; honest

_____ **17.** word: _____:
v. to hold the interest of and give pleasure to; to amuse; to think about or consider; to give hospitality to guests

_____ **18.** word: _____:
n. a written work; the main part of a piece of writing

_____ **19.** word: _____:
v. to think well of; to understand; to recognize the worth of and to be grateful for; to raise the price or value of

_____ **20.** word: _____:
n. a system of writing for the blind in which the fingers are used to read

COLUMN B

(A) I dive off *Calypso.* I swim underwater with a scuba tank on my back. "Is this a **genuine** experience? Am I really here?" I ask myself.

(B) "That sea elephant over there reminds me of the long-extinct **mammoth,** a woolly elephant. Am I dreaming?"

(C) I **appreciate** all the tips and advice that the crew gave me. I am grateful because it is my first solo dive. I begin to adjust to the light. Many strange sights float past me.

(D) The crew **informed** me just last night that I had to find the lost treasure. Why didn't they tell me sooner?

(E) Suddenly, a shark crosses my path. I **entertain** the idea of going back to the surface and to the safety of the ship. Then I think about the importance of my mission.

(F) My dive has been an **inspiration** to me. I suddenly feel creative! I am going to write a book about my adventures.

(G) What will my book be about? The **theme** will be the wonders of the sea, but its exact title will have to wait until later.

(H) My sister will insist that my book be put into **braille,** a system of writing that she can read by touch.

(I) The **text,** or the words, of the book will be easy to put into braille with a special typewriter.

(J) The **visual** part of the book, the photographs and drawings I make, will appear in full color. I wake up. . . . Cousteau's book, *The Shark: Splendid Savage of the Sea,* lies next to my bed. I guess it was only a dream.

EXERCISE 3 _Like Meanings and Opposite Meanings_ ✍️

Directions. For each item below, circle the letter of the choice that means the same, or about the same, as the boldface word.

21. an **inspiration** to us
- (A) burden
- (B) comfort
- (C) bitter disappointment
- (D) strong influence

22. a **visual** image
- (A) painted
- (B) something that can be seen
- (C) connected with touch
- (D) invisible to the human eye

23. the **theme** of the story
- (A) last paragraph
- (B) hidden threat
- (C) main idea
- (D) level of interest

24. to read **braille**
- (A) a system of writing for the blind
- (B) a very ancient form of writing
- (C) a military code
- (D) sign language

25. to read the **text**
- (A) written work
- (B) title
- (C) introduction
- (D) sign language

Directions. For each item below, circle the letter of the choice that means the opposite, or about the opposite, of the boldface word.

26. a **mammoth** fish
- (A) gentle
- (B) tiny
- (C) intelligent
- (D) endangered

27. to **appreciate** someone's help
- (A) scorn
- (B) understand
- (C) protect
- (D) imagine

28. to be **entertained** by dolphins
- (A) interested
- (B) studied
- (C) photographed
- (D) bored

29. a **genuine** interest
- (A) valuable
- (B) strong
- (C) fake
- (D) real

30. to **inform** the captain
- (A) withhold facts from
- (B) speak to quietly
- (C) answer directly
- (D) discuss openly with

MAKING NEW WORDS YOUR OWN

Lesson 22 | **CONTEXT:** Ecology and Environment

What Is the Forecast for Brazil's Rain Forest?

The largest tropical rain forest in the world is located in Brazil's Amazon region. Many valuable woods and plants are found in this rain forest, as well as hundreds of species of animals. Today, Brazil's rain forest is threatened. Scientists worry that the mass cutting of trees may affect the world's climate and that many species of plants and animals may become extinct.

In the following exercises, you will have the opportunity to expand your vocabulary by reading about Brazil's rain forest. These ten Vocabulary Words will be used.

campaign	conscience	furious	plot	urge
characteristic	doubtless	juvenile	reduction	widespread

EXERCISE 1 *Wordbusting* ✍

Directions. Follow these instructions for this word and the nine words on the next page.
- Figure out the word's meaning by looking at its **context**, its **structure**, and its **sound**. Fill in at least one of the three **CSS** boxes. Alternate which boxes you complete.
- Then, look up the word in a dictionary, read all of its meanings, and write the meaning of the word as it is used in the sentence.
- Follow this same process for each of the Vocabulary Words on the next page. You will need to draw your own map for each word. Use a separate sheet of paper.

1.

campaign → A **campaign** to save the rain forests is underway. People hope to achieve the goal of saving the tropical forests through a series of planned actions.

Context:

Structure:

Sound:

Dictionary:

2.
characteristic →
A major **characteristic** of Brazil's rain forest is the canopy. This unique feature is formed by the overlapping tops of trees. It acts as an umbrella over the forest.

3.
juvenile →
In the forest, **juvenile** trees are dwarfed by taller ones. These young trees have to struggle to find sunlight.

4.
doubtless →
Doubtless, many miners, farmers, and others will continue to resist efforts to save the rain forest. Of course, these people are concerned about making a living. They are afraid of what will happen if their activities are limited by the government.

5.
plot →
Farmers have burned trees on certain **plots** in the rain forest. They then plant crops on these areas of ground.

6.
furious →
Many of Brazil's farmers become extremely angry when they are told not to burn down trees in the rain forest. They feel that they have a right to earn a living and are **furious** when people tell them they cannot farm there.

7.
widespread →
Scientists worry that the destruction of the rain forests will have **widespread** effect. In fact, they expect the results to be felt all around the world.

8.
reduction →
Less burning of the rain forest would lead to a **reduction** in the amount of carbon dioxide in the air. Too much carbon dioxide might lead to global warming.

9.
conscience →
You must decide for yourself whether the destruction of the rain forest should be stopped. Let your **conscience** help you decide what is right and what is wrong.

10.
urge →
I **urge** you to find out as much as you can about the tropical rain forests. Once you have, you may want to persuade others to do the same.

EXERCISE 2   *Context Clues* 🖎

Directions. Scan the definitions in Column A. Then, think about how the boldface words are used in the sentences in Column B. To complete the exercise, match each definition in Column A with the correct Vocabulary Word from Column B. Write the letter of your choice on the line provided. Finally, write the Vocabulary Word on the line before the definition.

COLUMN A	COLUMN B

COLUMN A

_____ **11.** word: _____:
adj. young, immature, childish;
n. a young person, child or youth

_____ **12.** word: _____:
adv. certainly; probably; *adj.* sure

_____ **13.** word: _____:
n. a lessening; anything made by lessening something; the amount by which something is made smaller

_____ **14.** word: _____:
n. a small area of ground marked off for special use; a plan to do something dishonest; a story line; *v.* to plan secretly

_____ **15.** word: _____:
adj. occurring over a wide area; widely distributed or spread

_____ **16.** word: _____:
adj. full of rage; moving violently; intense

_____ **17.** word: _____:
n. a series of planned actions to achieve a goal; *v.* to promote a person actively for political office; to promote a cause

_____ **18.** word: _____:
adj. typical; *n.* a distinguishing feature

_____ **19.** word: _____:
v. to beg or plead; to persuade; to call forth; *v.* an impulse to do a certain thing

_____ **20.** word: _____:
n. a knowledge or sense of right and wrong, with a leaning toward doing right

COLUMN B

(A) Some people **plot** to smuggle endangered birds and other animals into the United States. They make their plans secretly because smuggling is a crime.

(B) A **characteristic** or normal day in the rain forest is very warm and humid. There is always a good chance that it will rain.

(C) The rain forest frequently experiences **furious,** or intense, thunderstorms.

(D) Cattle ranching and farming are becoming **widespread** in Brazil. Throughout the rain forest, huge ranches are appearing.

(E) A **reduction** in the number of trees in the rain forest means that fewer birds can nest there. Fewer trees will cause problems for monkeys and other animals, too.

(F) One environmentalist had an **urge** to write to Brazilian officials. From that sudden act, she eventually organized a meeting of top government leaders.

(G) **Doubtless,** much of Brazil's rain forest will be destroyed, probably within the next few years.

(H) **Juveniles** in the United States might not understand how the destruction of the rain forest touches them. It is hard for young people to see how something happening thousands of miles away can change their lives.

(I) If you were running for political office in Brazil, would you **campaign** to save the rain forest? Or would you put forward some other cause?

(J) The **consciences** of Brazil's elected officials will probably seal the fate of the rain forest. They have to balance what is right today with what is right for the future.

EXERCISE 3 *Like Meanings and Opposite Meanings*

Directions. For each item below, circle the letter of the choice that means the same, or about the same, as the boldface word.

21. a **campaign** to save the rain forest
   (A) most important goal
   (B) planned actions
   (C) desire
   (D) end result

22. the **conscience** of the voters
   (A) knowledge of the world
   (B) concerns about nature
   (C) sense of right and wrong
   (D) lack of power

23. a **furious** biologist
   (A) active
   (B) well-educated
   (C) secretive
   (D) very angry

24. the **plot** of a novel about Brazil
   (A) author
   (B) publisher
   (C) story line
   (D) last chapter

25. an **urge** to speak
   (A) impulse
   (B) request
   (C) permission
   (D) reason

Directions. For each item below, circle the letter of the choice that means the opposite, or about the opposite, of the boldface word.

26. a **characteristic** gesture
   (A) kind
   (B) unusual
   (C) inexperienced
   (D) youthful

27. **doubtless,** action must be taken
   (A) eagerly
   (B) maybe
   (C) sadly
   (D) impatiently

28. a **juvenile** worker
   (A) elderly
   (B) poor
   (C) native
   (D) working

29. a **reduction** of species
   (A) increase
   (B) count
   (C) small number
   (D) decrease

30. **widespread** logging
   (A) environmentally safe
   (B) limited by law
   (C) restricted
   (D) widely practiced

MAKING NEW WORDS YOUR OWN

Lesson 23 | **CONTEXT:** Ecology and Environment

Jean of the Environment: Jean Craighead George

"Save the whales!" "Recycle your plastic!" Today, the environment is a major topic of conversation, study, and even advertising. Jean Craighead George (b. 1919) helps younger readers learn about the environment while entertaining them with her novels and nonfiction books. George explores the Yu'pik and Inupiat cultures in Alaska and the Seminole culture in Florida. Her book, *My Side of the Mountain,* is the story of a boy who survives in the wilderness by living in a hollow tree trunk for a year.

In the following exercises, you will have the opportunity to expand your vocabulary by reading about Jean Craighead George. These ten Vocabulary Words will be used.

applaud	inexpensive	persuade	remedy	temporary
guidance	issue	protest	revolution	villain

EXERCISE 1 | *Wordbusting* 👉

Directions. Follow these instructions for this word and the nine words on the next page.
- Figure out the word's meaning by looking at its **context,** its **structure,** and its **sound.** Fill in at least one of the three **CSS** boxes. Alternate which boxes you complete.
- Then, look up the word in a dictionary, read all of its meanings, and write the meaning of the word as it is used in the sentence.
- Follow this same process for each of the Vocabulary Words on the next page. You will need to draw your own map for each word. Use a separate sheet of paper.

1.

(applaud) → Book reviewers **applaud** Jean Craighead George's writing. In fact, *Julie of the Wolves,* a novel about a Native Alaskan girl, received high praise: It was awarded the Newbery Medal in 1972.

Context:	Structure:	Sound:

Dictionary:

Name _____ Date _____ Class _____

2.

issue

In her book, *Who Really Killed Cock Robin? An Ecological Mystery,* George talks about the **issue** of chemical pollution and its far-reaching effects. The question of pollution and other current environmental topics are often themes in George's books.

3.

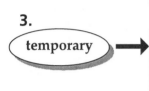
temporary

In *One Day in the Alpine Tundra,* George gives us a glimpse of a meadow in the mountains of Wyoming. Damage to that fragile world of plants and animals may be only **temporary.** How can we be sure the damage will not be permanent?

4.

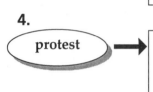
protest

Some people **protest**, or demonstrate, against environmental dangers. Others, like Jean Craighead George, have chosen to study and write about nature.

5.

persuade

George does not try to **persuade,** or convince, people to care about nature. She merely takes us to spend the winter with a pack of wolves or to search for food with baby alligators.

6.

villain

George avoids blaming **villains** in her stories. Instead of pointing to specific "bad guys," she coaxes her readers to understand the impact of their actions on nature.

7.

revolution

Some people think it will take a **revolution** to bring about the drastic changes needed to save our planet, but people like George work to bring about change in a peaceful way.

8.

guidance

Under George's **guidance,** her children carried out projects to learn more about nature. With their mother's advice, one son started his own chemical-free garden.

9.

inexpensive

Fortunately, there are many **inexpensive** ways to become a naturalist. You can make a bird feeder, study trees, plant flowers, or collect insects. All of these are very low-cost ways of starting an environmental project.

10.

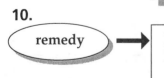
remedy

Knowledge is a **remedy** for many environmental problems, but knowledge without action cannot cure ills.

EXERCISE 2 Context Clues ✍

Directions. Scan the definitions in Column A. Then, think about how the boldface words are used in the sentences in Column B. To complete the exercise, match each definition in Column A with the correct Vocabulary Word from Column B. Write the letter of your choice on the line provided. Finally, write the Vocabulary Word on the line before the definition.

COLUMN A	COLUMN B

COLUMN A

_____ **11.** word: _____:
adj. costing little; low-priced; cheap

_____ **12.** word: _____:
v. to put forth or distribute; to publish;
n. a question to be decided; something put out in many copies; offspring

_____ **13.** word: _____:
v. to cause to do something; to convince

_____ **14.** word: _____:
v. to speak strongly against; to object;
n. an objection; a demonstration against

_____ **15.** word: _____:
v. to show enjoyment or approval by clapping hands; to praise

_____ **16.** word: _____:
n. leadership; advice and assistance

_____ **17.** word: _____:
n. a person who commits great crimes; a wicked or evil person; a criminal

_____ **18.** word: _____:
n. the movement of an object around another object; a turning motion; the forceful overthrow of a government; complete or radical change

_____ **19.** word: _____:
n. a cure or correction; *v.* to cure or correct

_____ **20.** word: _____:
adj. lasting for only a certain time; not permanent

COLUMN B

(A) Dear Ms. George:
Our sixth-grade class plans to **issue** a video magazine on the environment. We will put the first one out next month and would like to have your opinion on our ideas.

(B) The magazine will be **inexpensive,** because our costs are low. The only profit we seek is a healthier world.

(C) We plan to report on environmental **protests** because we think that people are interested in knowing who speaks out against polluters.

(D) We will ask how the protesters plan to **remedy** the problems that concern them. Then we will compare their solutions with those offered by experts in the environmental field.

(E) Do you think protesters can **persuade** people to change their old habits, or do you think that demonstrating is not the way to convince people to change?

(F) What if everyone started to recycle plastic? We think it would be a real **revolution,** and we hope our video magazine will help bring about this great change.

(G) In the video, we will also offer our audience some **guidance** on recycling. We believe people need some direction and help in this area.

(H) After all, our planet is not a **temporary** home. If we plan on the human race being here for good, we need to care for the earth.

(I) We will also name some of the **villains** in the environmental game, such as people who pollute our air, soil, or water.

(J) We hope that students will **applaud** when they see our video. We hope that adults will be pleased and will clap for us, too.

EXERCISE 3   *Like Meanings and Opposite Meanings* ✍

Directions. For each item below, circle the letter of the choice that means the same, or about the same, as the boldface word.

21. to **issue** a new book
(A) publish
(B) write
(C) buy
(D) read

22. a violent **revolution**
(A) disaster
(B) overthrow of the government
(C) complete stop
(D) election of the president

23. helpful **guidance**
(A) question
(B) work
(C) advice
(D) knowledge

24. to **persuade** them to change
(A) begin
(B) attempt
(C) wish
(D) convince

25. to **applaud** her effort
(A) understand
(B) watch over
(C) approve of
(D) help with

Directions. For each item below, circle the letter of the choice that means the opposite, or about the opposite, of the boldface word.

26. to **remedy** the situation
(A) correct
(B) worsen
(C) explain
(D) notice

27. an **inexpensive** product
(A) necessary
(B) cheap
(C) costly
(D) dangerous

28. to **protest** the decision
(A) praise
(B) object to
(C) make
(D) change

29. the story's **villain**
(A) character
(B) writer
(C) criminal
(D) hero

30. a **temporary** solution
(A) permanent
(B) brief
(C) sudden
(D) poor

MAKING NEW WORDS YOUR OWN

Lesson 24 **CONTEXT:** Ecology and Environment

Balancing Society and the Environment: Global Warming

A blanket of carbon dioxide and other gases surrounds the earth. This blanket is part of the earth's atmosphere and has warmed the earth for many thousands of years. Originally, the gases were produced by natural processes. For example, a volcanic eruption releases carbon dioxide into the air. Some of this gas is then used by green plants or absorbed by the ocean. The rest rises into the atmosphere and becomes part of the blanket.

In the following exercises, you will have the opportunity to expand your vocabulary by reading about global warming. These ten Vocabulary Words will be used.

adjust	candidate	disgust	employer	hazard
ballot	corporation	dissolve	foul	merchandise

EXERCISE 1 *Wordbusting*

Directions. Follow these instructions for this word and the nine words on the next page.
- Figure out the word's meaning by looking at its **context,** its **structure,** and its **sound.** Fill in at least one of the three **CSS** boxes. Alternate which boxes you complete.
- Then, look up the word in a dictionary, read all of its meanings, and write the meaning of the word as it is used in the sentence.
- Follow this same process for each of the Vocabulary Words on the next page. You will need to draw your own map for each word. Use a separate sheet of paper.

1.

adjust → Many scientists believe the earth's blanket of carbon dioxide is out of balance. These scientists say that if we don't **adjust,** or change, our behavior, global warming may result.

Context:	Structure:	Sound:

Dictionary:

2.

(hazard) →

> The blanket of gases is becoming thicker, environmentalists say. As a result, the earth may be getting warmer. Global warming would be a **hazard,** endangering plants and animals.

3.

(corporation) →

> Scientists say that some industries contribute to possible global warming more than others. Some **corporations** burn a lot of coal, oil, or gas.

4.

(disgust) →

> Many people feel **disgust** at the sight of litter on the highway, but other threats to the environment do not seem sickening at all. They come from things we take for granted, like automobiles and airplanes.

5.

(dissolve) →

> Cars use fossil fuel that releases gases into the air. Scientists say that we must change our everyday habits. Our environmental problems will not just **dissolve,** or fade away, into thin air.

6.

(merchandise) →

> Environmentalists tell us that one way to protect the environment is to use products that do not contribute to global warming. These products are environmentally friendly **merchandise.**

7.

(employer) →

> Changing our behavior is difficult, however, especially when a company that is a major **employer** is forced to make changes that lead to a loss of jobs.

8.

(foul) →

> We must not continue to **foul** our environment. Environmentalists say that we can help stop pollution and prevent global warming if we develop cleaner technologies and conserve energy.

9.

(ballot) →

> One way that we can change our behavior is by conserving, or saving, energy. Because our government can make laws that deal with conservation, people can express their views on the environment through the **ballot,** or vote.

10.

(candidate) →

> Many **candidates** who run for government offices want to protect the environment. They feel that a healthy, balanced environment is in everyone's best interest.

EXERCISE 2 *Context Clues* ✍

Directions. Scan the definitions in Column A. Then, think about how the boldface words are used in the sentences in Column B. To complete the exercise, match each definition in Column A with the correct Vocabulary Word from Column B. Write the letter of your choice on the line provided. Finally, write the Vocabulary Word on the line before the definition.

COLUMN A	COLUMN B
_____ **11.** word: _____: *n.* a danger; an obstacle; *v.* to attempt	(A) When gasoline is burned, carbon dioxide is released. Carbon dioxide **dissolves** into the air and becomes part of the blanket surrounding the earth.
_____ **12.** word: _____: *v.* to break up; to disappear	(B) In everyday life, it is almost impossible to notice carbon dioxide. Unlike many gases, it has no **foul** smell. Carbon dioxide is odorless.
_____ **13.** word: _____: *n.* a ticket by which a vote is cast; a list of people running for office	(C) **Employers** can help to cut down on pollution by encouraging the people who work for them to carpool or ride buses to their jobs.
_____ **14.** word: _____: *v.* to change so as to fit; to become used to	(D) Many **corporations** encourage workers to ride bicycles to work. These businesses provide special parking spaces for the bikes.
_____ **15.** word: _____: *adj.* offensive to the senses; dirty; evil; unfavorable; (in baseball) not fair; *v.* to cause or to become dirty or rotten	(E) Not all products that are **merchandised** as environmentally safe are truly safe. We must not be fooled by tricky methods of selling goods.
_____ **16.** word: _____: *n.* a person who seeks or is proposed for an office, award, and so on; a person or thing destined for a certain end	(F) If you want to buy environmentally friendly goods, do not just **hazard** a guess as to which products are really safe. Educate yourself.
_____ **17.** word: _____: *n.* goods that are bought and sold; *v.* to trade on or advertise a particular product	(G) It may be hard to **adjust** to a new way of shopping. Many people are not used to looking for environmentally friendly products.
_____ **18.** word: _____: *n.* a business firm or organization that is run by a group of people and that has many of the legal rights of an individual	(H) Pollution **disgusts** most people. If we do not change our behavior, say environmentalists, pollution will become even more sickening.
_____ **19.** word: _____: *n.* a person, business firm, and so on, that hires people to work for wages or salary	(I) In an election, environmental laws are often an item on the **ballot**. Some people vote based on what impact the laws will have on jobs. Others consider the laws' effect on the environment.
_____ **20.** word: _____: *n.* a feeling of extreme distaste or dislike; *v.* to sicken	(J) Environmentalists say that we must work to prevent global warming. If we do not, the earth will become a **candidate** for worldwide environmental problems—a sad destiny for all of us.

EXERCISE 3 *Like Meanings and Opposite Meanings* ✍

Directions. For each item below, circle the letter of the choice that means the same, or about the same, as the boldface word.

21. the store's **merchandise**
  (A) location
  (B) goods
  (C) popularity
  (D) recycling bin

22. to **adjust** the temperature
  (A) study scientifically
  (B) increase
  (C) correct or change
  (D) lower gradually

23. to mark the **ballot**
  (A) legal contract
  (B) sworn statement by a politician
  (C) ticket by which a vote is cast
  (D) driver's license

24. the new **corporation**
  (A) tax system
  (B) government agency that studies the law
  (C) court of law
  (D) business firm

25. the **candidate** for president
  (A) person who seeks office
  (B) president's trusted advisor
  (C) someone who studies the weather
  (D) famous person

Directions. For each item below, circle the letter of the choice that means the opposite, or about the opposite, of the boldface word.

26. to **dissolve**
  (A) stay solid
  (B) eat with water
  (C) use as fuel
  (D) study carefully

27. an understanding **employer**
  (A) high school teacher
  (B) neighbor
  (C) worker
  (D) partner

28. a health **hazard**
  (A) risk
  (B) mistake
  (C) mystery
  (D) safety

29. filled with **disgust**
  (A) pleasure
  (B) sense of doubt
  (C) feeling of hatred
  (D) shock

30. a **foul** smell
  (A) pleasing
  (B) dim
  (C) incredible
  (D) hopeful

MAKING NEW WORDS YOUR OWN

Lesson 25 CONTEXT: Ecology and Environment
The Arabian Oryx and Other Endangered Species

The Arabian oryx is a kind of antelope with long, straight horns. It is one of the few animals that lives in the Arabian desert. For years, it has been hunted for sport. The Phoenix Zoo saved the animal from extinction by starting a breeding herd. The antelopes were then reintroduced into their native habitat. Many species, however, have become extinct, or wiped out, while the populations of others have declined. What can be done to save these animals?

In the following exercises, you will have the opportunity to expand your vocabulary by reading about endangered wildlife. These ten Vocabulary Words will be used.

absorb	cooperate	mourning	omit	security
complaint	debt	offense	regret	tension

EXERCISE 1 Wordbusting

Directions. Follow these instructions for this word and the nine words on the next page.
- Figure out the word's meaning by looking at its **context**, its **structure**, and its **sound**. Fill in at least one of the three **CSS** boxes. Alternate which boxes you complete.
- Then, look up the word in a dictionary, read all of its meanings, and write the meaning of the word as it is used in the sentence.
- Follow this same process for each of the Vocabulary Words on the next page. You will need to draw your own map for each word. Use a separate sheet of paper.

1.

absorb → Because so many of the earth's species are threatened with extinction today, it is hard to **absorb** all the facts about them. It takes some time for the information to sink in and make sense.

Context:	Structure:	Sound:

Dictionary:

2.

(complaint) ➤ Many **complaints** are filed against people who export endangered animals such as the woolly monkey. These protests rarely lead to action, however.

3.

(tension) ➤ People await the return of the whooping cranes to the Texas coast every year with great **tension**. They feel a strain not knowing how many birds will survive the long journey from Canada.

4.

(omit) ➤ It would be a mistake to **omit** the Japanese crested ibis and the noisy scrub bird from the endangered species list. They are both in danger of extinction.

5.

(regret) ➤ Those people who nearly wiped out the oryx should **regret** their actions. I wonder how many of them feel sorry about what they did.

6.

(security) ➤ Some endangered animals find **security** only in zoos, where they are protected from danger.

7.

(mourning) ➤ When endangered species in zoos do not bear live young, there is **mourning,** or grief, for the loss of a species.

8.

(offense) ➤ Some biologists have taken the **offense** in the fight to save endangered animals. They think more animals might become extinct unless the problems are attacked right away.

9.

(cooperate) ➤ Several nations began to **cooperate** in wildlife conservation after the United Nations was formed in 1945. They realized they needed to work together in order to protect endangered species.

10.

(debt) ➤ The Nature Conservancy and other groups have been buying wilderness land from countries that are in **debt**. The countries then use the money to pay what they owe, and land that endangered species live on is protected.

Name _____ Date _____ Class _____

EXERCISE 2 *Context Clues* ✍

Directions. Scan the definitions in Column A. Then, think about how the boldface words are used in the sentences in Column B. To complete the exercise, match each definition in Column A with the correct Vocabulary Word from Column B. Write the letter of your choice on the line provided. Finally, write the Vocabulary Word on the line before the definition.

COLUMN A

_____ **11.** word: _____:
n. a protest; a written or spoken expression of pain, annoyance, or discontent

_____ **12.** word: _____:
n. the expression of grief at someone's death; the period during which one grieves for the dead; *adj.* of grief

_____ **13.** word: _____:
v. to soak up; to take up the attention of

_____ **14.** word: _____:
n. a strain; a state of strained relations

_____ **15.** word: _____:
v. to feel sorry about or mourn; to feel remorseful; *n.* a troubled feeling

_____ **16.** word: _____:
n. something owed by one person to another; the state of owing

_____ **17.** word: _____:
v. to leave out

_____ **18.** word: _____:
n. the feeling of being safe or certain; safety; an organization that guards an area; an assurance of repayment of a loan or debt

_____ **19.** word: _____:
v. to work with others for a shared cause or purpose

_____ **20.** word: _____:
n. a crime; the feeling of hurt; something that greatly upsets; the side that attacks

COLUMN B

(A) Many people live with a false sense of **security** about endangered animals. They are not aware that the numbers of certain species are dangerously low.

(B) There was a period of **mourning** when the last Carolina parakeet died in 1910. Many people grieved the loss of this beautiful bird.

(C) The hunting of the Javan rhinoceros is a serious **offense,** or crime.

(D) When talking about endangered animals, do not **omit** the Bali tiger of Indonesia. No endangered creature should be overlooked.

(E) Scientists are **absorbed** with the study of the pink pigeon of Mauritius. They pay close attention to how many of these pigeon chicks are hatched each year.

(F) **Tension** exists between poachers and those who want to protect endangered animals. These uneasy relations have sometimes resulted in violent conflicts.

(G) Scientists and government officials have **cooperated** in order to help the wild nenes of Hawaii. By working together, they have helped increase the population of this bird.

(H) Because humans have caused many species' disappearance, some environmentalists feel that we owe a **debt** to the species that remain.

(I) One way to help endangered animals is to send a written **complaint** to your local newspaper. Your letter should express your feelings about the trouble facing these animals.

(J) Feeling troubled about extinct animals will not bring them back. **Regret** can, however, cause people to act to protect today's endangered species.

EXERCISE 3 · Like Meanings and Opposite Meanings

Directions. For each item below, circle the letter of the choice that means the same, or about the same, as the boldface word.

21. the biologists' **complaint**
- (A) supporting statement
- (B) explanation
- (C) protest
- (D) key interview

22. a large **debt**
- (A) antelope
- (B) popular movement
- (C) woods beetle
- (D) amount owed

23. to **cooperate** to help the oryx
- (A) work together
- (B) protest
- (C) think of ways
- (D) decide

24. **mourning** extinct animals
- (A) painting
- (B) looking for
- (C) studying
- (D) grieving for

25. to **absorb** the information
- (A) present
- (B) soak up
- (C) dismiss
- (D) ask about

Directions. For each item below, circle the letter of the choice that means the opposite, or about the opposite, of the boldface word.

26. to **regret** the outcome
- (A) feel worried about
- (B) feel sorry about
- (C) feel afraid of
- (D) feel good about

27. to **omit** the giant panda
- (A) hunt
- (B) include
- (C) study
- (D) sketch

28. **security** for all animals
- (A) protection
- (B) hope
- (C) danger
- (D) zoos

29. the biologists' **offense**
- (A) fighters
- (B) offering
- (C) losers
- (D) defense

30. the **tension** between biologists and poachers
- (A) state of ease
- (B) discussions
- (C) state of strain
- (D) payment of debt

MAKING NEW WORDS YOUR OWN

Lesson 26 | **CONTEXT:** Ecology and Environment

Peter Rabbit Would Have Been Proud of Beatrix Potter

Do the names Peter Rabbit, Flopsy, Mopsy, and Cottontail sound familiar? They were all created by Beatrix Potter (1866–1943), a quiet woman who dearly loved both animals and children. Potter also loved the Lake District of England and wanted to preserve it. In her later years she became involved with the National Trust, which bought and cared for land so that the countryside would not be changed by development.

In the following exercises, you will have the opportunity to expand your vocabulary by reading about Beatrix Potter. These ten Vocabulary Words will be used.

amateur	intrusion	privacy	resident	simplify
duplicate	keen	rebel	self-respect	sympathy

EXERCISE 1 *Wordbusting*

Directions. Follow these instructions for this word and the nine words on the next page.
- Figure out the word's meaning by looking at its **context,** its **structure,** and its **sound.** Fill in at least one of the three **CSS** boxes. Alternate which boxes you complete.
- Then, look up the word in a dictionary, read all of its meanings, and write the meaning of the word as it is used in the sentence.
- Follow this same process for each of the Vocabulary Words on the next page. You will need to draw your own map for each word. Use a separate sheet of paper.

1.

amateur → In addition to writing and illustrating children's books, Beatrix Potter was an **amateur** scientific illustrator. Her hobby involved painting watercolors of plants and fungi.

Context:	Structure:	Sound:

Dictionary:

2.

duplicate → In her artwork, Potter tried to **duplicate** nature. She wanted the drawings to look exactly like what she saw.

3.

intrusion → Potter was a very private person who did not want **intrusion,** or interference, in her personal life.

4.

keen → Potter was always **keen** about animals and nature. Everyone around her was aware of her strong feelings on these subjects.

5.

privacy → Potter wrote her journals in code to protect her **privacy**. She wanted to be sure that the details of her personal life could not be made public.

6.

rebel → As a child, Potter always obeyed her parents and other adults; she was never a **rebel**.

7.

simplify → Potter told stories about her pet rabbit, Peter. To make sure the stories would be easy for children to understand, she **simplified** her language.

8.

resident → As a **resident** of the Lake Country, Potter had a special interest in it. She wanted to preserve the area that was her home.

9.

self-respect → Potter had healthy, positive feelings about herself and her accomplishments. She probably developed this strong sense of **self-respect** early in life.

10.

sympathy → Potter was in **sympathy** with the aims of the National Trust. She shared its belief that the Lake Country should be preserved.

EXERCISE 2 *Context Clues*

Directions. Scan the definitions in Column A. Then, think about how the boldface words are used in the sentences in Column B. To complete the exercise, match each definition in Column A with the correct Vocabulary Word from Column B. Write the letter of your choice on the line provided. Finally, write the Vocabulary Word on the line before the definition.

COLUMN A	COLUMN B

_____ **11.** word: _____:
n. a person who resists authority; *v.* to resist authority or control

_____ **12.** word: _____:
adj. exactly alike; *n.* an exact copy; *v.* to make an exact copy

_____ **13.** word: _____:
v. to make easier or less complex

_____ **14.** word: _____:
adj. living in a place for a period of time; **n.** a person who lives in a place

_____ **15.** word: _____:
n. a beginner, not a professional; **adj.** of or done by someone acting for pleasure rather than for pay

_____ **16.** word: _____:
n. the act of forcing oneself on others; an unasked-for interruption

_____ **17.** word: _____:
n. a withdrawal from public company; one's private life; secrecy

_____ **18.** word: _____:
n. a sameness in feeling; a feeling of agreement with an idea

_____ **19.** word: _____:
n. a high regard for oneself and one's worth as a person

_____ **20.** word: _____:
adj. sharp; shrewd; strongly felt; enthusiastic

(A) Potter wanted children to have **self-respect,** to have a sense of their own worth.

(B) Potter first told the story of Peter Rabbit in a letter. **Duplicates** of the story, along with exact copies of her original pictures, were later printed in a book.

(C) Potter had a **keen** sense of pleasure in the way of life in the countryside. She felt a deep connection to the land.

(D) Potter was an **amateur** naturalist. She studied nature for her own pleasure.

(E) Although she enjoyed her **privacy,** Potter also liked the company of others.

(F) Potter had **sympathy** with those who felt it was important to preserve the countryside. She shared their belief in its worth.

(G) As an adult, Potter became a **rebel.** She resisted the control of developers in the countryside.

(H) Potter was concerned about the **intrusion** of developers into the rural Lake Country. By buying land and preserving it, she blocked their attempt to force themselves into the area.

(I) Potter wanted to give the parcels of land she bought to the National Trust. To **simplify** the process, she left all the land to the Trust when she died, rather than hand it over bit by bit while she was still alive.

(J) A **resident** conservationist, Potter picked up litter and planted trees in her own neighborhood during the last ten years of her life.

EXERCISE 3   *Like Meanings and Opposite Meanings* ✍

Directions. For each item below, circle the letter of the choice that means the same, or about the same, as the boldface word.

21. to **duplicate** Potter's journal

(A) copy
(B) decode
(C) create
(D) read

22. an unwelcome **intrusion**

(A) group
(B) interruption
(C) following
(D) question

23. **keen** about Peter Rabbit

(A) enthusiastic
(B) worried
(C) very friendly
(D) afraid

24. not lacking **self-respect**

(A) selfishness
(B) bravery
(C) high regard for oneself
(D) care for others

25. a **sympathy** with children

(A) shared understanding
(B) desired result
(C) playfulness
(D) a deep sense of loneliness

Directions. For each item below, circle the letter of the choice that means the opposite, or about the opposite, of the boldface word.

26. an **amateur** writer

(A) professional
(B) intelligent
(C) unknown
(D) poor

27. a desire for **privacy**

(A) friendship
(B) children
(C) secrecy
(D) company

28. to **rebel** against nature

(A) obey
(B) resist
(C) speak
(D) study

29. a **resident** children's author

(A) popular
(B) quiet
(C) young
(D) visiting

30. to **simplify** the language for children

(A) newly invent
(B) listen to
(C) make harder
(D) speak clearly

MAKING NEW WORDS YOUR OWN

Lesson 27 | CONTEXT: Ecology and Environment

Pandas: Cute Is Not Everything

Giant pandas are adorable, with black ears, noses, and eye patches. If you have seen one you are lucky, for they are very rare. Pandas live in the mountain forests of China, where they eat mostly bamboo shoots. There used to be thousands of them. Today, only about a thousand wild pandas live in a small area. China gave two pandas—Ling-Ling and Hsing-Hsing—to the United States. Both lived at the National Zoo until they died in the 1990s. The Chinese government has also loaned pandas to a few U.S. wildlife parks.

In the following exercises, you will have the opportunity to expand your vocabulary by reading about pandas. These ten Vocabulary Words will be used.

captivity	eavesdrop	prey	provoke	threat
decrease	migrate	prohibit	survival	tragedy

EXERCISE 1 *Wordbusting*

Directions. Follow these instructions for this word and the nine words on the next page.
- Figure out the word's meaning by looking at its **context,** its **structure,** and its **sound.** Fill in at least one of the three **CSS** boxes. Alternate which boxes you complete.
- Then, look up the word in a dictionary, read all of its meanings, and write the meaning of the word as it is used in the sentence.
- Follow this same process for each of the Vocabulary Words on the next page. You will need to draw your own map for each word. Use a separate sheet of paper.

1.

(captivity) → Only a few giant pandas live in **captivity** today. Although they are not free, they are safe and protected.

Context:	Structure:	Sound:

Dictionary:

2.

(decrease) ➔ The number of giant pandas in the wild has **decreased**. It has fallen to about one thousand and may continue to fall.

3.

(eavesdrop) ➔ Scientists use radio collars to keep track of pandas. The radios do not allow scientists to **eavesdrop** on, or hear, the bears, only to locate them.

4.

(prey) ➔ Giant pandas have been the **prey** of hunters, who have shot them for their fur.

5.

(provoke) ➔ What could **provoke** hunters to kill pandas? The answer is obvious: As long as people are willing to buy their fur, the pandas will be in danger.

6.

(prohibit) ➔ The Chinese government now **prohibits** hunting the giant panda. It wants to prevent hunters from wiping out the pandas.

7.

(threat) ➔ People are a **threat** to the giant pandas in several ways. Even if people do not hunt the animals, they can cause great harm to them by cutting down forests.

8.

(survival) ➔ The **survival** of giant pandas in the wild depends on the supply of bamboo. When the bamboo is cut down, many pandas will die of starvation.

9.

(migrate) ➔ Pandas have had to **migrate** as forests have been cut. If they do not move from place to place, they are not able to find food.

10.

(tragedy) ➔ It is always a **tragedy** when a panda dies in the wild. Because there are so few pandas, the death of a young panda is an even worse disaster.

EXERCISE 2 *Context Clues* ✍

Directions. Scan the definitions in Column A. Then, think about how the boldface words are used in the sentences in Column B. To complete the exercise, match each definition in Column A with the correct Vocabulary Word from Column B. Write the letter of your choice on the line provided. Finally, write the Vocabulary Word on the line before the definition.

COLUMN A	COLUMN B

COLUMN A

_____ **11.** word: _____:
n. to listen secretly to a private conversation

_____ **12.** word: _____:
n. imprisonment; the condition of being held against one's will

_____ **13.** word: _____:
n. the act or fact of living or existing

_____ **14.** word: _____:
n. an animal hunted and killed for food by another animal; a person or thing that is hunted; *v.* to hunt or kill for food; to rob; to weigh heavily (upon)

_____ **15.** word: _____:
v. to become smaller; to lessen; *n.* a lessening

_____ **16.** word: _____:
n. a statement or action of intended harm; an indication of danger

_____ **17.** word: _____:
v. to refuse to permit; to prevent

_____ **18.** word: _____:
n. an event bringing great suffering; a disaster; a serious play about such events

_____ **19.** word: _____:
v. to cause action; to stir up feelings; to irritate

_____ **20.** word: _____:
v. to move from one place to another

COLUMN B

(A) The dangers facing the giant pandas **prey** on, or disturb, the minds of environmentalists.

(B) The **survival** of the giant pandas cannot be taken for granted. Without our help, they may not live.

(C) Public awareness of the pandas' situation should **provoke** the necessary action to save them. Awareness is always the first step in causing changes to occur.

(D) When the pandas run out of food, they sometimes **migrate** from the mountain forests to farmland to find more to eat.

(E) A **decrease,** or decline, of human settlements in the mountains would probably help the giant pandas.

(F) Hungry wild pandas are sometimes captured and fed to **prohibit** them from starving.

(G) The Chinese government has made **threats** to those who think about hunting pandas. The government warns that hunters will be severely punished.

(H) About forty giant pandas live in **captivity** around the world. If they could choose, I am sure they would rather live in freedom in the mountain forests of China!

(I) The story of the little panda cub crushed by its mother is very sad. It is a subject on which a playwright could base a **tragedy.**

(J) At wildlife parks with pandas, if you **eavesdrop,** you can always overhear people talk about how cute the bears are.

EXERCISE 3 *Like Meanings and Opposite Meanings*

Directions. For each item below, circle the letter of the choice that means the same, or about the same, as the boldface word.

21. the **captivity** of endangered species
    (A) freedom
    (B) health
    (C) imprisonment
    (D) value

22. to **eavesdrop** on the conversation
    (A) listen
    (B) interrupt
    (C) whisper
    (D) repeat

23. to **provoke** another
    (A) produce
    (B) deny
    (C) cease
    (D) annoy

24. the lion **preys**
    (A) escapes
    (B) is killed
    (C) sleeps
    (D) hunts

25. a **decrease** in the number of pandas
    (A) mistake
    (B) lessening
    (C) increase
    (D) change

Directions. For each item below, circle the letter of the choice that means the opposite, or about the opposite, of the boldface word.

26. to make a **threat**
    (A) example
    (B) assurance
    (C) disaster
    (D) statement

27. to **migrate** in search of food
    (A) move from place to place
    (B) make noises
    (C) stay in one place
    (D) roll over logs

28. to **prohibit** hunting
    (A) expect
    (B) allow
    (C) dislike
    (D) license

29. **survival** in zoos
    (A) dying off
    (B) existing
    (C) breeding
    (D) playing

30. the **tragedy** of the rare panda
    (A) disaster
    (B) story
    (C) death
    (D) comedy

MAKING NEW WORDS YOUR OWN

Lesson 28 | **CONTEXT:** Ecology and Environment
Catching the Sun for Energy

Where do we get unlimited, free energy? One source is the sun, which we often take for granted. As the earth gets more crowded and there are fewer energy resources, people are starting to look toward the sun. As a result, someday you may live in a solar house! Its enormous windows would face south. Your water would be heated by flat plates that collect heat from the sun. In summer, your home could be air-conditioned with solar power.

In the following exercises, you will have the opportunity to expand your vocabulary by reading about solar energy. These ten Vocabulary Words will be used.

| benefit | reckless | responsibility | suburbs | unite |
| obvious | resemble | severe | unfortunate | vocal |

EXERCISE 1 | *Wordbusting* ✍

Directions. Follow these instructions for this word and the nine words on the next page.
- Figure out the word's meaning by looking at its **context,** its **structure,** and its **sound.** Fill in at least one of the three **CSS** boxes. Alternate which boxes you complete.
- Then, look up the word in a dictionary, read all of its meanings, and write the meaning of the word as it is used in the sentence.
- Follow this same process for each of the Vocabulary Words on the next page. You will need to draw your own map for each word. Use a separate sheet of paper.

1.

(benefit) → A clear **benefit** of solar energy is that it does not cause pollution. In this way it is an improvement over the burning of oil and coal.

| Context: | Structure: | Sound: |

| Dictionary: |

2.
obvious →

It is **obvious** that we will have to develop new kinds of energy. Clearly, the earth is running out of fuels like oil that cannot be renewed.

3.
reckless →

We can no longer be **reckless** with the earth's resources. We must be careful and think about the future.

4.
responsibility →

The **responsibility** for developing clean energy sources lies with us. We have a duty to protect the environment now so that future generations can enjoy it.

5.
severe →

There were **severe** shortages of oil and natural gas during the 1970s and 1980s. These serious shortages sped up the development of solar technology.

6.
suburbs →

New solar homes are being built in many American **suburbs**. It is often less expensive to build such homes outside city limits.

7.
resemble →

Solar homes **resemble** homes that are powered by electricity. From the outside, they look very much the same, but flat panels on the roof usually show that a home uses solar power.

8.
unite →

Solar furnaces are made up of several mirrors that **unite** to focus the sun's rays on one spot. Bringing together energy collected by these mirrors can generate electricity.

9.
vocal →

Many builders are **vocal** about the advantages of solar energy. They speak out about its low cost and its lack of pollution.

10.
unfortunate →

It is **unfortunate** that so few people make use of solar energy. It is unlucky for our environment that we remain tied to oil and gas.

EXERCISE 2 *Context Clues* ✍

Directions. Scan the definitions in Column A. Then, think about how the boldface words are used in the sentences in Column B. To complete the exercise, match each definition in Column A with the correct Vocabulary Word from Column B. Write the letter of your choice on the line provided. Finally, write the Vocabulary Word on the line before the definition.

COLUMN A	COLUMN B

COLUMN A

_____ **11.** word: _____:
n. the areas just outside a city; the towns surrounding a city

_____ **12.** word: _____:
adj. easy to see or understand; evident

_____ **13.** word: _____:
adj. capable of making sounds; connected to the voice; inclined to express oneself with speech

_____ **14.** word: _____:
adj. having or bringing bad luck; not favorable; unlucky

_____ **15.** word: _____:
n. something that adds to the improvement of a condition; an event to raise money for a cause; *v.* to do good to

_____ **16.** word: _____:
adj. careless; not caring about future results

_____ **17.** word: _____:
n. the state of being dependable; an obligation; a duty

_____ **18.** word: _____:
v. to bring or join together for a common cause; to make into one

_____ **19.** word: _____:
v. to be similar to; to look like

_____ **20.** word: _____:
adj. serious; strict or very critical

COLUMN B

(A) Everyone should accept the **responsibility** of saving energy. This is an important duty.

(B) To use only fossil fuels for energy is **reckless;** people need to develop alternative sources of energy.

(C) Scientists and engineers have **united** to study solar energy. Together they have made progress.

(D) Solar energy is caused by nuclear reactions that take place in the sun. The reactions **resemble,** or are like, the reactions that take place in nuclear bombs.

(E) Sadly, we use only a small fraction of the solar energy that reaches the earth. It is **unfortunate** that we have not found more ways to harness it.

(F) Solar cells power many small electronic devices, such as calculators. One **obvious** advantage is that you never need to replace the batteries. A clear drawback is that they need light in order to work.

(G) In 1940, the first solar home was built in a **suburb** near Chicago.

(H) A **benefit** was held recently to raise money for solar energy research. The governor was the guest of honor.

(I) The tone of the governor's speech was **severe.** Looking stern, she told us that we should support solar energy research.

(J) Before the event, **vocal** supporters of solar energy formed a rally. You could hear their voices from several blocks away.

EXERCISE 3 *Like Meanings and Opposite Meanings* ✍

Directions. For each item below, circle the letter of the choice that means the same, or about the same, as the boldface word.

21. to **benefit** the environment
  (A) do good for
  (B) speak out for
  (C) clean up
  (D) write about

22. to **resemble** nuclear energy
  (A) create
  (B) control
  (C) contrast with
  (D) be similar to

23. a **responsibility** to future generations
  (A) letter
  (B) duty
  (C) friend
  (D) release

24. a **severe** shortage of funding
  (A) improved
  (B) unknown
  (C) serious
  (D) mild

25. to **unite** different groups
  (A) form
  (B) split apart
  (C) speak to
  (D) bring together

Directions. For each item below, circle the letter of the choice that means the opposite, or about the opposite, of the boldface word.

26. an **obvious** advantage
  (A) cheap
  (B) related
  (C) unclear
  (D) free

27. the **reckless** use of resources
  (A) careful
  (B) gradual
  (C) careless
  (D) generous

28. homes in the **suburbs**
  (A) national parks
  (B) inner cities
  (C) mountains
  (D) seashores

29. an **unfortunate** event
  (A) expected
  (B) lucky
  (C) exciting
  (D) popular

30. a **vocal** supporter
  (A) young
  (B) shouting
  (C) tired
  (D) silent

MAKING NEW WORDS YOUR OWN

Lesson 29 | **CONTEXT:** Ecology and Environment

For the People and for the Future: U.S. National Parks

If not for Yellowstone's famous geysers, we might not have a National Park System. In 1870, fabulous tales of these geysers prompted General Henry D. Washburn to visit the area. Another man, Judge Cornelius Hedges, suggested that the land should be protected from mining and lumbering. Two years later, Yellowstone became the first national park. Today, many types of natural and historic sites are preserved.

In the following exercises, you will have the opportunity to expand your vocabulary by reading about the United States' national parks. These ten Vocabulary Words will be used.

anthem	courteous	justify	promotion	rehearsal
compliment	engage	nominate	qualify	specify

EXERCISE 1 *Wordbusting*

Directions. Follow these instructions for this word and the nine words on the next page.
- Figure out the word's meaning by looking at its **context,** its **structure,** and its **sound.** Fill in at least one of the three **CSS** boxes. Alternate which boxes you complete.
- Then, look up the word in a dictionary, read all of its meanings, and write the meaning of the word as it is used in the sentence.
- Follow this same process for each of the Vocabulary Words on the next page. You will need to draw your own map for each word. Use a separate sheet of paper.

1.

(anthem) → Have you ever heard the song "America the Beautiful"? It is probably the best-known **anthem** to the magnificence of the United States. Do you recall the memorable words praising the sky and mountains?

Context:

Structure:

Sound:

Dictionary:

Name _____ Date _____ Class _____

2.

compliment → Those words of praise are not simply a formal **compliment**. Instead, they express the heartfelt feelings of millions of people.

3.

justify → Today, nature has become precious. Many animals have become endangered. Fragile beaches are at risk. What reason can **justify** their destruction?

4.

nominate → To protect our natural wealth, we must **nominate** and elect people who will conserve our heritage. The future depends on how we manage our resources today.

5.

courteous → In fact, the United States was the first nation to have a national park. Now, over 350 parks are protected. **Courteous** park rangers politely give visitors information about the natural features of the parks.

6.
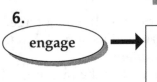
engage → In the parks, anyone can find sights to **engage** the senses. What tourist has not been charmed and captivated by the majesty of the Grand Canyon?

7.

promotion → The National Park Service need not attract visitors through advertising or other types of **promotion**. In fact, the parks regularly fill up and have to turn campers away.

8.

qualify → Most parks require an entrance fee. However, people sixty-two years of age or older can enter free with a Golden Age Passport. Likewise, people with physical impairments may **qualify** for a Golden Access Passport and free entry.

9.
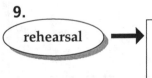
rehearsal → If you want to visit a national park, be sure to plan ahead. New campers are often surprised at the difficulty. If you want to set up a wilderness camp, you might plan a **rehearsal** near your home as practice for the real thing.

10.

specify → In some areas, cabins, motels, and hotels are available. You need to make your reservations months early! Remember to **specify** dates and your exact needs.

EXERCISE 2 *Context Clues*

Directions. Scan the definitions in Column A. Then, think about how the boldface words are used in the sentences in Column B. To complete the exercise, match each definition in Column A with the correct Vocabulary Word from Column B. Write the letter of your choice on the line provided. Finally, write the Vocabulary Word on the line before the definition.

COLUMN A	COLUMN B

COLUMN A

_____ **11.** word: _____:
n. a song of praise or devotion

_____ **12.** word: _____:
n. something said in admiration, praise, or flattery; *v.* to congratulate; to praise

_____ **13.** word: _____:
n. a repeating for practice before a future performance or event; a practice

_____ **14.** word: _____:
v. to name or appoint to a position

_____ **15.** word: _____:
v. to draw into; to fascinate; to enter in conflict with; to take part in; to hire

_____ **16.** word: _____:
n. an advancement in rank or pay; the furthering of a cause; the advertisement of a product or event

_____ **17.** word: _____:
adj. polite and considerate towards others; well-mannered

_____ **18.** word: _____:
v. to show to be just, right, and reasonable

_____ **19.** word: _____:
v. to define, mention, or describe in detail; state definitely

_____ **20.** word: _____:
v. to explain by narrowing down or describing the specific characteristics of; to be fit for a position

COLUMN B

(A) Before I give an oral report, I like to have a **rehearsal**. I asked my mother to listen to a run-through of my draft.

(B) "Imagine the last notes of the national **anthem** fading away," I told her, to set the tone. Then I began my speech.

(C) "Ladies and gentlemen, I would like to tell you about Big Bend National Park. Its beauty alone **justifies,** or is reason for, its membership in our National Parks System.

(D) "Let me **specify** the benefits it offers. Over 800,000 acres of unspoiled land await visitors. The park contains desert, springs, and the Rio Grande.

(E) "During my visit, we **engaged** a guide to lead us through some of the rougher country. This hired guide led us through Boquillas Canyon.

(F) "Our **courteous** guide was not only thoughtful, he was extremely knowledgeable about the fossils that can be found in the park.

(G) To **qualify** for a job here, you need to be very well informed about the park.

(H) All the wildlife at Big Bend—beaver, deer, and the rare panther—are well protected. I **compliment** the staff of Big Bend. They deserve praise for their good work.

(I) "They guard some of our most priceless treasures. In my opinion, they should all receive **promotions** to advance their careers.

(J) "I hope that we continue to **nominate,** or name, such responsible people to safeguard the future of this great bend in the Rio Grande."

EXERCISE 3 *Like Meanings and Opposite Meanings* 👉

Directions. For each item below, circle the letter of the choice that means the same, or about the same, as the boldface word.

21. to **justify** your actions
   (A) plan ahead
   (B) describe in detail
   (C) show reasons for
   (D) recall to mind

22. to proudly **nominate**
   (A) approach boldly
   (B) accept a prize
   (C) name as a candidate
   (D) give a speech

23. a hurried **rehearsal**
   (A) funeral
   (B) practice
   (C) turnaround
   (D) graduation

24. the national **anthem**
   (A) constitution
   (B) military
   (C) song
   (D) flag

25. to **qualify** for a job
   (A) announce in advance
   (B) research in detail
   (C) make a good argument
   (D) be suited for

Directions. For each item below, circle the letter of the choice that means the opposite, or about the opposite, of the boldface word.

26. to **specify** details
   (A) generalize
   (B) measure
   (C) memorize
   (D) attend to

27. her **promotion** of the project
   (A) hurrying
   (B) creation
   (C) opinion
   (D) blocking

28. a **compliment** to the chef
   (A) insult
   (B) tragedy
   (C) message
   (D) essay

29. to **engage** in conflict
   (A) draw swords
   (B) withdraw
   (C) bully
   (D) maintain

30. a **courteous** attitude
   (A) polite
   (B) foolish
   (C) rude
   (D) serious

MAKING NEW WORDS YOUR OWN

Lesson 30 | **CONTEXT:** Ecology and Environment

Making the Great Lakes Great Again

Superior, Michigan, Huron, Erie, and Ontario are the five Great Lakes. These lakes border eight states: Minnesota, Wisconsin, Michigan, Illinois, Indiana, Ohio, Pennsylvania, and New York. The Great Lakes are among the fifteen largest lakes in the world. If you stand on the shore of any one of them, it will seem as if you are standing at the edge of an ocean. In fact, the lakes are so large that they are sometimes called inland seas.

In the following exercises, you will have the opportunity to expand your vocabulary by reading about the Great Lakes. These ten Vocabulary Words will be used.

| apologize | associate | hesitate | pollute | superior |
| application | frantic | impatience | reservoir | toxic |

EXERCISE 1 *Wordbusting* ✍

Directions. Follow these instructions for this word and the nine words on the next page.
- Figure out the word's meaning by looking at its **context,** its **structure,** and its **sound.** Fill in at least one of the three **CSS** boxes. Alternate which boxes you complete.
- Then, look up the word in a dictionary, read all of its meanings, and write the meaning of the word as it is used in the sentence.
- Follow this same process for each of the Vocabulary Words on the next page. You will need to draw your own map for each word. Use a separate sheet of paper.

1.

(apologize) → Some companies **apologize** for the past pollution of the Great Lakes. Their regrets, combined with stricter regulations, have visibly improved water quality in the lakes.

| Context: | Structure: | Sound: |

Dictionary:

2.

application →

Scientists hope that the **application** of new technology will help to reduce the effects of pollution. Putting these new technologies into practice may help cut pollution at its source.

3.

associate →

Are your friends and classmates concerned about pollution? Talk to the people you **associate** with about the pollution problem in the Great Lakes.

4.

frantic →

Many people who live near the Great Lakes are very concerned with the safety of their homes. As water levels in the lakes rise steadily, lake-shore residents are **frantic** with worry that they will lose their homes to the lake.

5.

hesitate →

Lakeshore homeowners feel that there is no time to lose. They call for quick action, urging the government not to **hesitate** in reducing water levels.

6.

impatience →

It's not hard to understand the **impatience** of these homeowners. They hate any delay because in a few years' time their houses may be swallowed by the lakes.

7.

pollute →

Some people feel that protecting the environment should come first, and impure water is a major concern. They point out that industrial chemicals, municipal wastes, and runoff from rain **pollute** the waters in the United States.

8.

reservoir →

Pollution in the Great Lakes is threatening at least one water **reservoir**. High levels of dangerous chemicals have been found in the water supply.

9.

superior →

Today, knowledge of the Great Lakes' environmental problems is **superior** to that of any time in the past. Thanks to modern science, we have the best and most thorough knowledge of the lakes ever.

10.

toxic →

Now we know that many of the wastes discharged into the Great Lakes are **toxic** to humans and other species. If fish die as a result of these harmful wastes, how can the water be safe for humans?

EXERCISE 2 *Context Clues* ✍

Directions. Scan the definitions in Column A. Then, think about how the boldface words are used in the sentences in Column B. To complete the exercise, match each definition in Column A with the correct Vocabulary Word from Column B. Write the letter of your choice on the line provided. Finally, write the Vocabulary Word on the line before the definition.

COLUMN A	COLUMN B
____ 11. word: _____: *v.* to join with others; to connect different things together; *n.* a person with whom one works; *adj.* having less than full status	(A) It is a sunny fall day on Lake Erie. Sixteen sixth-grade students are filled with **impatience** as they line up to climb aboard a small tugboat. They cannot wait to start their trip!
____ 12. word: _____: *adj.* poisonous; giving harm	(B) Finally, the captains of the boat arrive. They are sorry for their lateness, and they **apologize**.
____ 13. word: _____: *v.* to express regret for a fault or wrong	(C) The captains, Pat and Chuck Potter, are **reservoirs** of valuable information about the Great Lakes area. They have a great supply of facts and figures memorized.
____ 14. word: _____: *adj.* wild with anger, pain, or worry	(D) Pat tells the students that they should **associate** the foamy water they see at the base of a low dam with pollution. There is a definite connection.
____ 15. word: _____: *n.* a place where water is collected and stored ; a large supply of something	(E) The students do not **hesitate** at guessing the source of the pollution. They instantly remember the nearby factories.
____ 16. word: _____: *v.* to make dirty; to make impure or corrupt	(F) Pat explains the causes of this poisonous pollution. She says that many of the factories have been releasing **toxic** wastes into the lakes for years.
____ 17. word: _____: *v.* to pause or stop momentarily; to delay because of feeling unsure	(G) Pat points out a fertilizer plant. "That plant has just filled out an **application** for a new waste dump. The paperwork has been completed."
____ 18. word: _____: *adj.* high or higher in order, status, or rank; greater in quality or value	(H) "The old dump has already killed the surrounding plants. We are working at a **frantic** pace to see that no new dumps are allowed. We are trying to beat the clock."
____ 19. word: _____: *n.* the method of putting something to use; continued effort; a form to be filled out with information	(I) Pat reminds us that strict U.S. regulations on pollution are **superior** to those in Canada. As a result, some U.S. companies go there to dump their wastes.
____ 20. word: _____: *n.* annoyance because of delay; restless eagerness to do something	(J) On the return trip, the students agreed that it was sad to realize how many harmful wastes have **polluted** the Great Lakes.

EXERCISE 3   *Like Meanings and Opposite Meanings*

Directions. For each item below, circle the letter of the choice that means the same, or about the same, as the boldface word.

21. the polluted **reservoir**
   (A) river that runs into one of the Great Lakes
   (B) treatment plant for impure water
   (C) a factory that creates smog
   (D) water supply

22. the **application** of new technology
   (A) use
   (B) discovery
   (C) understanding
   (D) scientific method

23. to **pollute** the mind
   (A) educate
   (B) dirty
   (C) destroy
   (D) weaken

24. her business **associate**
   (A) admirer
   (B) office
   (C) enemy
   (D) partner

25. do not **hesitate**
   (A) wait briefly
   (B) fall suddenly
   (C) enter quickly
   (D) cry loudly

Directions. For each item below, circle the letter of the choice that means the opposite, or about the opposite, of the boldface word.

26. to **apologize** for one's actions
   (A) have regret
   (B) be proud
   (C) resist
   (D) repeat

27. the **toxic** chemicals
   (A) deadly
   (B) weak
   (C) harmful
   (D) harmless

28. our growing **impatience**
   (A) anger
   (B) patience
   (C) impossibility
   (D) unhappiness

29. a **frantic** attempt
   (A) violent
   (B) foolish
   (C) frenzied
   (D) calm

30. a **superior** method
   (A) faster
   (B) uncertain
   (C) worse
   (D) better

INTRODUCTION

UNDERSTANDING NEW WORDS AND THEIR USES

Building Your Vocabulary

One way to build your vocabulary is to learn the different meanings of a single word. Another way is to learn how to make new words by using prefixes and suffixes. A third way is to learn about the origins of words. Learning about the origins of words will help you remember the words' meanings. The following exercises will help you build on, and remember, vocabulary.

HOW TO DO EXERCISE 1   *Multimeaning*

Words often have more than one meaning. In a Multimeaning exercise, you will read a boldface Vocabulary Word in a sentence. You will then read four more sentences that use the same Vocabulary Word. Your job is to choose the sentence that uses the Vocabulary Word in the same way as it is used in the first sentence. Here is an example of a Multimeaning exercise:

The fog of nineteenth-century London was, in fact, **foul** air caused by pollution.
- **(A)** Soot from the city's many chimneys would also **foul** the air.
- **(B)** In this setting, Detective Sherlock Holmes tracks down **foul** murderers and other evil-doers.
- **(C)** Nothing keeps Holmes from the chase. He goes out into the streets of London even in a thunderstorm or other **foul** weather.
- **(D)** Waste dumped into London's river Thames had made the waterway **foul**.

In the first sentence, the air was **foul** because of pollution. Pollution makes things dirty or impure. **Foul** is used as an adjective to mean dirty or impure. How does this compare to the uses of the word in choices A, B, C, and D?

- In choice A, **foul** is a verb meaning to pollute or make dirty.
- In choice B, **foul** means evil, not dirty.
- In choice C, **foul** is used to describe weather, and it means unfavorable or stormy.
- In the correct choice, D, **foul** again describes something made dirty or impure.

HOW TO DO EXERCISE 2   *Word Analysis*

Prefixes and Suffixes

The following items will give you practice in identifying the kinds of prefixes and suffixes that you will run into again and again as you read. In each of these items, you will read two words. Both words will contain the same prefix or suffix. You will be asked to identify the choice that describes the meaning of the prefix or suffix as it is used in both words. Here is an example of a prefix exercise:

readjust   **re**write
(A) after
(B) with
(C) before
(D) again

Hint #1 The second word will usually be a word that you already know well. For example, you probably already know that *rewrite* means "to write again."

Hint #2 The first word or its root (in this case, *adjust*) is a word you learned in *Making New Words Your Own*. When you remember that *rewrite* means "to write again," you can guess that *readjust* means "to adjust again." That leads you to the correct choice, D.

Note: The tables in the front of this book list some common prefixes and suffixes. These tables will help you to complete the exercises on *Prefixes* and *Suffixes* in the lessons that follow.

Word Origins

Many words in the English language come from Greek, Latin, French, and other languages. Word Origins exercises will give you practice in learning the roots of Vocabulary Words. In these exercises, you will be asked to identify the choice that best completes the sentence.

Here is an example of a Word Origins exercise:

debt   decrease   definite   descriptive

The Latin word *crescere*, "to grow," combined with the prefix *de–*, "away," gives us the word _____.

Hint #1 Compare the Latin root to the list of words provided above the item. If you remove *de–* from all of the choices, the part of the word left that most resembles the Latin root would be *–crease*, from the word *decrease*.

Hint #2 The choices in Word Origins will be Vocabulary Words you studied in *Making New Words Your Own*. In the introduction to *Making New Words Your Own*, you learned that to decrease means "to grow smaller." *Decrease* is the correct response.

UNDERSTANDING NEW WORDS AND THEIR USES

Lesson 1 **CONTEXT:** Amazing Nature

Has Anyone Seen the Abominable Snowman?

EXERCISE 1 *Multimeaning*

Directions. Read each numbered sentence below. Then, circle the letter of the choice that uses the boldface word in the same way as it is used in the numbered sentence.

1. Would you like to **interview** the author of the new best-selling book about the Abominable Snowman?
   (A) During his **interview** for the job of forest ranger, my brother was asked his opinion about Bigfoot.
   (B) Following the most recent sighting of the Loch Ness monster, the police granted an **interview** to the national news media.
   (C) If I could go to Africa, I would **interview** some people who claim to have seen a dinosaur in Lake Telle.
   (D) The **interview** on the morning talk show revealed some fascinating information about huge flying reptiles seen in Asia.

2. The morning **session** of the conference included a talk by a scientist who studies unusual sea creatures.
   (A) During its fall **session,** the college offered a course on mysterious creatures of the world.
   (B) The conference's most interesting **session,** which was held from ten to eleven o'clock, was about the book *On the Track of Unknown Animals* by Bernard Heuvelmans.
   (C) It was just after a **session** of wood-chopping that Mr. Brehm claims to have seen Bigfoot.
   (D) A bill to protect the Bigfoot was proposed when the state's legislature was in **session** from August to September.

EXERCISE 2 *Word Analysis*

Prefixes

Directions. Read each numbered pair of words below. Then, circle the letter of the choice that best describes the meaning of the underlined prefix as it is used in each pair.

3. <u>in</u>definite   <u>in</u>complete
   (A) not
   (B) less
   (C) very
   (D) beyond

4. <u>un</u>expectedly   <u>un</u>interested
   (A) very
   (B) with
   (C) not
   (D) greater than

Suffixes

Directions. Read each numbered pair of words below. Then, circle the letter of the choice that best describes the meaning of the underlined suffix as it is used in each pair.

5. summar**ize**   magnet**ize**
   (A) undo
   (B) without
   (C) person who does
   (D) make

6. reli**able**   undeni**able**
   (A) full of
   (B) practice of
   (C) able to be
   (D) about

Word Origins

Directions. Read each of the following sentences. Then, from the vocabulary list below, choose the word that best completes the sentence. Write the word in the blank.

astonish	doubtful	majority	summarize
conference	innumerable	navigator	symbol
definite	interview	quote	twilight
deny	journalism	reliable	unexpectedly
descendant	legend	session	vivid

7. The Middle English word *astonien,* meaning "to stun," carries over into Modern English as the word _____.

8. The Latin word *denagare* means "to say no," as does the English word _____.

9. By combining the Latin word *numerus,* meaning "number," the prefix *in-,* meaning "not," and the suffix *-able,* meaning "able to be," we get the English word _____.

10. The Middle English word *liht,* meaning "to shine," is combined with the Old English word *twi* to form the Modern English word _____.

UNDERSTANDING NEW WORDS AND THEIR USES

| Lesson 2 | **CONTEXT:** Amazing Nature |

Traveling Down Tornado Alley

| **EXERCISE 1** | *Multimeaning* |

Directions. Read each numbered sentence below. Then, circle the letter of the choice that uses the boldface word in the same way as it is used in the numbered sentence.

1. To see a good **demonstration** of how a tornado forms, go to the Mid-America Museum in Hot Springs, Arkansas.
   (A) Following the deadly tornadoes, the people staged a **demonstration** in front of city hall to protest the city's safety procedures.
   (B) After our home was destroyed by a tornado, we appreciated the community's sincere **demonstration** of concern.
   (C) The salesperson's **demonstration** failed to convince us that the fence could withstand a tornado.
   (D) The **demonstration** against the new law was postponed because a tornado was sighted south of town.

2. The tornado's 200-mile-per-hour winds ripped the little store right off its **foundation**.
   (A) The tornado picked up a car and set it down on the **foundation** of a nearby house that had been blown away.
   (B) The family established the charitable **foundation** to help victims of natural disasters such as tornadoes.
   (C) There is a **foundation** in actual events for describing one section of the country as Tornado Alley.
   (D) The **foundation** of our Emergency Readiness Team is the preparedness of its members.

| **EXERCISE 2** | *Word Analysis* |

Prefixes

Directions. Read each numbered pair of words below. Then, circle the letter of the choice that best describes the meaning of the underlined prefix as it is used in each pair.

3. <u>un</u>detected   <u>un</u>happy
   (A) against
   (B) extremely
   (C) not
   (D) into

4. <u>co</u>incidental   <u>co</u>operate
   (A) together
   (B) able
   (C) without
   (D) act

Suffixes

Directions. Read each numbered pair of words below. Then, circle the letter of the choice that best describes the meaning of the underlined suffix as it is used in each pair.

5. detect<u>ion</u>   depress<u>ion</u>
(A) like
(B) state of
(C) person who does
(D) study of

6. predict<u>able</u>   forgett<u>able</u>
(A) not capable of being
(B) against
(C) capable of being
(D) act of

Word Origins

Directions. Read each of the following sentences. Then, from the vocabulary list below, choose the word that best completes the sentence. Write the word in the blank.

aviation	departure	fatal	miraculous
collapse	detect	foundation	nuisance
collide	disastrous	incident	predict
complex	disturb	instinct	rash
demonstration	exception	locally	unfavorable

7. The Middle English word *nusance,* meaning "annoyance," became the Modern English word _____.

8. We get a hint of the meaning of the word _____ when we learn that the Latin word *avis* means "bird."

9. The Latin word *collidere,* meaning "to strike together," is related to our word _____.

10. You may recognize the Latin *instinctus,* meaning "instigation," "prompt," or "enthusiasm" in the Modern English word _____.

UNDERSTANDING NEW WORDS AND THEIR USES

Lesson 3 **CONTEXT:** Amazing Nature

Tangled in a Spider's Web

EXERCISE 1 *Multimeaning* ✍

Directions. Read each numbered sentence below. Then, circle the letter of the choice that uses the boldface word in the same way as it is used in the numbered sentence.

1. I would like for you to **escort** me through the passage—it is full of spiders.
    (A) My sister's **escort** for the prom looks like Jeff Daniels, the actor who starred in the movie *Arachnophobia,* which is about the fear of spiders.
    (B) I had to **escort** my little brother and his Cub Scout troop through the museum's spider house.
    (C) As their **escort,** I told the group the common name for each spider, such as the wolf spider and the crab spider.
    (D) When the museum's rare spider collection was transferred to another museum, it was given a police **escort.**

2. Since the 1950s, each **generation** of young readers has enjoyed the book *Charlotte's Web* by E. B. White.
    (A) The speaker said that the **generation,** or production, of new pesticides is harmful to spiders.
    (B) Some scientists have spent their careers studying the **generation,** or procreation, of spiders.
    (C) I think our **generation** is less frightened of spiders than people my grandparents' age, but I could be wrong.
    (D) The university's **generation** of money for research of spider habits was slow.

EXERCISE 2 *Word Analysis* ✍

Prefixes

Directions. Read each numbered pair of words below. Then, circle the letter of the choice that best describes the meaning of the underlined prefix as it is used in each pair.

3. <u>re</u>involve   <u>re</u>read
    (A) lacking
    (B) with
    (C) not
    (D) again

4. <u>im</u>mobile   <u>im</u>patient
    (A) very
    (B) toward
    (C) not
    (D) with

Suffixes

Directions. Read each numbered pair of words below. Then, circle the letter of the choice that best describes the meaning of the underlined suffix as it is used in each pair.

5. hero<u>ic</u>   fantast<u>ic</u>
   (A) unrelated to
   (B) state of being
   (C) of or related to
   (D) somewhat

6. separat<u>ion</u>   complet<u>ion</u>
   (A) act of
   (B) unable to
   (C) able to
   (D) full of

Word Origins

Directions. Read each of the following sentences. Then, from the vocabulary list below, choose the word that best completes the sentence. Write the word in the blank.

abdomen	dread	generation	maximum
caution	error	gratitude	mobile
commotion	escort	heroic	paralysis
competition	flexible	hoist	previous
congratulate	foe	involve	separation

7. Not much was changed in the Middle English word *fo,* meaning "enemy," to make our Modern English word _____.

8. From the Greek word *paralyein,* meaning "to weaken," we get our English word _____.

9. The Latin word *errare,* which means "to go astray," gives us the English word _____.

10. We can still see the Latin word *congratulari,* meaning "to rejoice with someone," in the English word _____.

UNDERSTANDING NEW WORDS AND THEIR USES

Lesson 4 **CONTEXT: Amazing Nature**

Wild About Animals

EXERCISE 1 *Multimeaning*

Directions. Read each numbered sentence below. Then, circle the letter of the choice that uses the boldface word in the same way as it is used in the numbered sentence.

1. I became curious about beavers when my teacher made **reference** to the amazing dams they build using wood and mud.
   - (A) *Wild Animals of North America,* published by the National Geographic Society, is an excellent **reference** book.
   - (B) My cousin Tanya, a dolphin trainer, received a glowing **reference** from her former boss for her new job with the sea-life park.
   - (C) I'm going to use Dr. Nabors, a retired biologist, as a **reference** for my report about weaver ants.
   - (D) Your **reference** to armadillos jumping when they are startled reminded me of a funny cartoon.

2. During our trip to Australia, we saw three kangaroos **vault** a fence, easily clearing it.
   - (A) Drawings of cats, which were sacred to the ancient Egyptians, were found on the inner walls of the **vault**.
   - (B) The **vault** of the snow leopard is a wonder to behold.
   - (C) Would you like to see a snow leopard **vault** a snowy canyon?
   - (D) The photographer kept the negatives of the award-winning pictures of the duckbill platypus in a **vault** at the bank.

EXERCISE 2 *Word Analysis*

Prefixes

Directions. Read each numbered pair of words below. Then, circle the letter of the choice that best describes the meaning of the underlined prefix as it is used in each pair.

3. <u>dis</u>comfort   <u>dis</u>approve
   - (A) for
   - (B) after
   - (C) opposite
   - (D) into

4. <u>de</u>regulate   <u>de</u>frost
   - (A) undo
   - (B) do the same as
   - (C) do more than
   - (D) state of

Suffixes

Directions. Read each numbered pair of words below. Then, circle the letter of the choice that best describes the meaning of the underlined suffix as it is used in each pair.

5. imitat<u>ive</u>   competit<u>ive</u>
   (A) tending to
   (B) resulting in
   (C) not like
   (D) one who does

6. conceal**ment**   excite**ment**
   (A) state of
   (B) without being
   (C) suitable for
   (D) resulting in

Word Origins

Directions. Read each of the following sentences. Then, from the vocabulary list below, choose the word that best completes the sentence. Write the word in the blank.

assault	disguise	impostor	regulate
conceal	earnest	inhale	requirement
dainty	gasp	linger	terminal
discomfort	hibernate	portion	vacuum
discourage	imitate	reference	vault

7. The Latin word *imponere*, meaning "place up on," has given us the English word

_____ .

8. Our English word _____ comes from the Old Norse word *geispa*, which means "a short catching of the breath."

9. The Latin word *partio*, meaning "part," evolved into the English word

_____ .

10. The Middle English word *deinte*, which means "excellent," gives us the Modern English word _____ .

UNDERSTANDING NEW WORDS AND THEIR USES

Lesson 5 | CONTEXT: Amazing Nature

Einstein Started Somewhere, Too

EXERCISE 1 | *Multimeaning* ✍

Directions. Read each numbered sentence below. Then, circle the letter of the choice that uses the boldface word in the same way as it is used in the numbered sentence.

1. This year, a **toll** of one dollar was charged to process each entry in the regional science fair.
   - (A) I wanted to call my friend in Seattle to tell him about the science fair, but the **toll** was too much.
   - (B) Working night and day on her science fair entry really has taken a **toll** on Janice's health.
   - (C) For her project, Sabina decided to **toll** church bells and measure the time of sound vibrations.
   - (D) The rainstorm took a heavy **toll** on the number of people willing to come out to the science fair.

2. Because I do not have my driver's **license,** one of my parents drove me to the beach to get sea water for my experiment.
   - (A) "Who gave you **license** to use my bowls and measuring cups for your experiment?" my mother asked.
   - (B) One of my experiments involved cooking fresh-caught fish, so I had to get a fishing **license**.
   - (C) In order for the Fish and Game Department to **license** me, I had to have parental permission.
   - (D) My sister joked that the letters on our car **license** plate, YAE, must stand for "Young Albert Einstein."

EXERCISE 2 | *Word Analysis* ✍

Prefixes

Directions. Read each numbered pair of words below. Then, circle the letter of the choice that best describes the meaning of the underlined prefix as it is used in each pair.

3. <u>anti</u>static   <u>anti</u>freeze
   - (A) between
   - (B) for
   - (C) against
   - (D) together

4. <u>non</u>flammable   <u>non</u>fiction
   - (A) before
   - (B) very
   - (C) not
   - (D) against

Suffixes

Directions. Read each numbered pair of words below. Then, circle the letter of the choice that best describes the meaning of the underlined suffix as it is used in the pair.

5. suspic**ious**   courag**eous**
   (A) one who does
   (B) state of
   (C) away from
   (D) full of

6. surg**ery**   robb**ery**
   (A) act or practices of
   (B) extremely
   (C) one who does
   (D) of or pertaining to

Word Origins

Directions. Read each of the following sentences. Then, from the vocabulary list below, choose the word that best completes the sentence. Write the word in the blank.

bombard	jeopardy	pierce	static
bureau	license	pry	stray
conviction	lunar	ransom	surgery
flammable	particle	receipt	suspicion
gossip	pharmacy	resign	toll

7. The Old English word *godsibbe,* meaning "godparent," later came to be *godsip,* meaning "good friend." In Modern English, this word has become _____, something good friends often do.

8. *Raunson,* meaning "to buy back," is a Middle English word that became the Modern English word _____.

9. From the Latin word *recipere,* meaning "to receive," we get the word _____— a paper we receive to show we have paid for something.

10. You may recognize the French word *bombe,* meaning "bomb," in the Modern English word _____.

UNDERSTANDING NEW WORDS AND THEIR USES

Lesson 6 | **CONTEXT: People and Places**

A Career in Anthropology

EXERCISE 1 *Multimeaning*

Directions. Read each numbered sentence below. Then, circle the letter of the choice that uses the boldface word in the same way as it is used in the numbered sentence.

1. If you choose a **career** in anthropology, you could study people's physical or cultural characteristics.
   (A) You might study how in some cultures most people **career** through life, while in other cultures people prefer a slower pace.
   (B) The science of anthropology has moved through this century in full **career,** making rapid progress.
   (C) L.S.B. Leakey (1903–1972), who did much research in Africa, was a **career** anthropologist and archaeologist.
   (D) Mary Catherine Bateson (b. 1939), the daughter of famed anthropologist Margaret Mead (1901–1978), entered the same **career** as her mother.

2. An anthropologist's life can be extremely interesting, but there is always some **routine** involved with every job.
   (A) In her field work, Margaret Mead's **routine** varied somewhat with the locations.
   (B) The **routine** lives of members of a society are studied by anthropologists.
   (C) The actors presented a **routine** based on Margaret Mead's first encounters with young Samoan girls.
   (D) Traveling to faraway islands was a **routine** for Margaret Mead.

EXERCISE 2 *Word Analysis*

Prefixes

Directions. Read each numbered pair of words below. Then, circle the letter of the choice that best describes the meaning of the underlined prefix as it is used in each pair.

3. **pre**determined   **pre**arranged
   (A) against
   (B) into
   (C) before
   (D) after

4. **self**-confidence   **self**-guiding
   (A) regarding others
   (B) doubly
   (C) not of the self
   (D) of the self

Suffixes

Directions. Read each numbered pair of words below. Then, circle the letter of the choice that best describes the meaning of the underlined suffix as it is used in each pair.

5. react**ion**   confus**ion**
  (A) result of
  (B) capable of
  (C) without
  (D) before

6. respect**able**   think**able**
  (A) incapable of being
  (B) nearly
  (C) capable of being
  (D) full of

Word Origins

Directions. Read each of the following sentences. Then, from the vocabulary list below, choose the word that best completes the sentence. Write the word in the blank.

analyze	determination	notion	respectable
biography	document	offspring	routine
career	essential	profession	scholar
debate	generous	publicity	self-confidence
destination	identical	reaction	thorough

7. The Latin word *notio,* meaning "coming to know," has added one letter and changed meaning to become the English word _____.

8. We can easily see the French word *publicité,* meaning "public information," in the English word _____.

9. The French word *analyser,* which means "to separate into basic principles," gives us the English word _____.

10. There is not much difference in the Old English word *ofspring,* meaning "to spring from," and the Modern English word _____.

UNDERSTANDING NEW WORDS AND THEIR USES

Lesson 7 **CONTEXT: People and Places**

Mexico City: Then and Now

EXERCISE 1 *Multimeaning*

Directions. Read each numbered sentence below. Then, circle the letter of the choice that uses the boldface word in the same way as it is used in the numbered sentence.

1. Have you read about the **conduct** of the Aztecs during the terrible two-year drought that began in 1450?
   (A) It was the great King Montezuma I (1390?–1469?) who had to **conduct** the Aztecs' efforts to survive the drought years.
   (B) It was also up to the king to **conduct** the many military battles that extended the empire from the Pacific Ocean to the Gulf of Mexico.
   (C) Aztec parents taught their children important rules about **conduct**.
   (D) The musician will **conduct** his own composition, "Warriors of the Sun."

2. While hurrying through Mexico City's Chapultepec Park, did you **glimpse** the giant cypress known as the Tree of Montezuma?
   (A) Our tour allowed time for only a **glimpse** of the Alameda, the city's central park.
   (B) Fortunately, we had time for much more than a **glimpse** of the unearthed Great Temple of the Aztecs.
   (C) The air was hazy, so it was difficult to **glimpse** the mountains surrounding Mexico City.
   (D) Even a **glimpse** of the snow-covered peaks is impressive.

EXERCISE 2 *Word Analysis*

Prefixes

Directions. Read each numbered pair of words below. Then, circle the letter of the choice that best describes the meaning of the underlined prefix as it is used in each pair.

3. <u>re</u>ignite   <u>re</u>capture
   (A) before
   (B) never
   (C) first
   (D) again

4. <u>un</u>interrupted   <u>un</u>wanted
   (A) after
   (B) half
   (C) not
   (D) again

Suffixes

Directions. Read each numbered pair of words below. Then, circle the letter of the choice that best describes the meaning of the underlined suffix as it is used in each pair.

5. manage**ment**   arrange**ment**
   (A) unable to
   (B) act or state of
   (C) one who
   (D) into

6. sacrific**ial**   resident**ial**
   (A) not related to
   (B) state of
   (C) pertaining to
   (D) resulting in

Word Origins

Directions. Read each of the following sentences. Then, from the vocabulary list below, choose the word that best completes the sentence. Write the word in the blank.

architect	desperate	ignite	realm
betray	district	interrupt	sacrifice
ceremony	eternal	management	scheme
conduct	fragrant	plead	victim
consent	glimpse	quarantine	victorious

7. From the Greek word *architekton,* meaning "chief carpenter," comes the English word
_____.

8. The Modern English word _____ comes from the Middle English word *realme. Realme,* in turn, comes from the Latin word *regere,* meaning "to rule."

9. The Medieval Latin word *districtus,* meaning "an area of jurisdiction or rule," became the Modern English word _____.

10. Originally, the English word _____ meant "to isolate for forty days," because it came from the Italian word *quarantina,* meaning "forty days."

UNDERSTANDING NEW WORDS AND THEIR USES

Lesson 8   CONTEXT: People and Places
Rocky Roads and Snake River Canyon

EXERCISE 1   *Multimeaning*

Directions. Read each numbered sentence below. Then, circle the letter of the choice that uses the boldface word in the same way as it is used in the numbered sentence.

1. The magazine editors made a **survey** about people's knowledge of the Rocky Mountains.
   (A) It would be a big job to **survey** all 3,000 miles of the Rocky Mountains.
   (B) The **survey** proves that a wide variety of animals make the Rockies their home.
   (C) Government officials said they will **survey** the damage caused by forest fires in the Southern Rockies.
   (D) The Geological Service has to **survey** the mountains with instruments before section markers are put in place.

2. Many **dramatic** views of the mountains can be seen while traveling the Going-to-the-Sun Road in Glacier National Park.
   (A) At a local theater, we saw a **dramatic** production about mountaineers in the Rockies.
   (B) The lead actor, who made many sly comments directly to the audience, was a master of **dramatic** irony.
   (C) As we sat around the bonfire in our Rocky Mountain camp, each of us gave **dramatic** tellings of our earlier camping experiences.
   (D) Float trips near Jackson, Wyoming, provide views of some **dramatic** scenes in the Snake River Canyon.

EXERCISE 2   *Word Analysis* ✍

Prefixes

Directions. Read each numbered pair of words below. Then, circle the letter of the choice that best describes the meaning of the underlined prefix as it is used in each pair.

3. <u>extra</u>ordinary   <u>extra</u>terrestrial
   (A) less than
   (B) beyond
   (C) part of
   (D) different from

4. <u>ir</u>regular   <u>ir</u>responsible
   (A) between
   (B) within
   (C) extremely
   (D) not

Suffixes

Directions. Read each numbered pair of words below. Then, circle the letter of the choice that best describes the meaning of the underlined suffix as it is used in each pair.

5. establish**ment**   govern**ment**
  (A) process of
  (B) possession of
  (C) lack of
  (D) of or relating to

6. leisure**ly**   kind**ly**
  (A) state of
  (B) within
  (C) likeness
  (D) without

Word Origins

Directions. Read each of the following sentences. Then, from the vocabulary list below, choose the word that best completes the sentence. Write the word in the blank.

abundant	establish	irregular	prehistoric
barrier	extraordinary	leisure	satisfy
descriptive	feat	marvel	survey
desirable	flourish	numerous	terrain
dramatic	inaccurate	possess	vicinity

7. The Old French word *fait*, meaning "an act or deed," has become the English word

_____.

8. The Old French word *barriere*, meaning "bar," has become the English word

_____.

9. The old French word *merveille*, meaning "wonder," became the Middle English *marvail* and the Modern English word _____.

10. The Latin words *vicus*, meaning "village," and *vicinus*, meaning "near," helped form the English word _____.

UNDERSTANDING NEW WORDS AND THEIR USES

Lesson 9 | CONTEXT: People and Places

Dazzled by Diamonds

EXERCISE 1 *Multimeaning*

Directions. Read each numbered sentence below. Then, circle the letter of the choice that uses the boldface word in the same way as it is used in the numbered sentence.

1. Did the empress **request** her garnet or her opal earrings?
   (A) The sign in the museum states that detailed information about the queen's jewels is available on **request**.
   (B) The tour guide told a legend about one king's **request** that grains of solid gold be sprinkled in the duck pond.
   (C) Please **request** that the tour guide find out whether the emeralds are from Colombia.
   (D) Teresa's **request** is to see the pear-shaped Spoonmaker Diamond.

2. The dishonest man's plan was to **counterfeit** bills and use them to buy jewels.
   (A) Did he really **counterfeit** the jewels by using plastic and paint?
   (B) The saleswoman could tell that the customers' interest in the gems was **counterfeit**.
   (C) Experts verified that the three diamonds from South Africa were not **counterfeit**.
   (D) The **counterfeit** was detected quickly by the experienced jeweler.

EXERCISE 2 *Word Analysis*

Prefixes

Directions. Read each numbered pair of words below. Then, circle the letter of the choice that best describes the meaning of the underlined prefix as it is used in each pair.

3. <u>un</u>ambitious   <u>un</u>friendly
   (A) less
   (B) not
   (C) always
   (D) again

4. <u>dis</u>honorable   <u>dis</u>connected
   (A) nearly
   (B) opposite
   (C) of or relating to
   (D) away from

Suffixes

Directions. Read each numbered pair of words below. Then, circle the letter of the choice that best describes the meaning of the underlined suffix as it is used in the pair.

5. invest**ment**   pave**ment**
   (A) one who does
   (B) product or thing
   (C) into
   (D) bringing about

6. heir**ess**   princ**ess**
   (A) female
   (B) male
   (C) one who does
   (D) without

Word Origins

Directions. Read each of the following sentences. Then, from the vocabulary list below, choose the word that best completes the sentence. Write the word in the blank.

ambitious	heir	oath	request
arid	honorable	ornamental	solitary
counterfeit	investment	portrait	transparent
envy	knapsack	reign	wardrobe
exclaim	luxurious	relate	yacht

7. If you know that the *j* in the Dutch word *jaghte-schip* ("chasing ship") is pronounced as a *y*, then you will know the origin of the English word _____.

8. The Modern English word _____ comes from the Latin word *aridus*, meaning "to be dry."

9. The Middle English word *oth*, meaning "a solemn vow," became the Modern English word _____.

10. The Middle English word *knappen*, "to eat," and the Dutch word *zac*, or "sack," were combined to make the Dutch word *knapzak*. This word eventually came into Modern English as the word _____.

UNDERSTANDING NEW WORDS AND THEIR USES

Lesson 10 | **CONTEXT:** People and Places

Japan and The Japanese

EXERCISE 1 *Multimeaning* 👈

Directions. Read each numbered sentence below. Then, circle the letter of the choice that uses the boldface word in the same way as it is used in the numbered sentence.

1. I **assume** you know that the Japanese islands are located along the "Ring of Fire."
   - (A) Did his uncle **assume** the debts of the soybean farm in southern Japan?
   - (B) He will **assume** the management of the farm, too.
   - (C) The teacher should not **assume** that everyone in the class knows the names of Japan's four main islands.
   - (D) The women will **assume** traditional Japanese robes called *kimonos*.

2. It would be interesting to **contrast** farming methods in Japan with those in China.
   - (A) The book shows the basic **contrast** between the public gardens and parks in Japan and those in the United States.
   - (B) The **contrast** in this picture of Tokyo is not very good, so I cannot identify the details.
   - (C) In **contrast,** the fishing industry in Japan is modern.
   - (D) Will she **contrast** Mount Fuji with other volcanoes in Japan?

EXERCISE 2 *Word Analysis* 👈

Prefixes

Directions. Read each numbered pair of words below. Then, circle the letter of the choice that best describes the meaning of the underlined prefix as it is used in each pair.

3. <u>dis</u>advantage   <u>dis</u>loyalty
   - (A) like
   - (B) opposite of
   - (C) distant
   - (D) different

4. <u>in</u>accurate   <u>in</u>correct
   - (A) not
   - (B) into
   - (C) extremely
   - (D) often

Suffixes

Directions. Read each numbered pair of words below. Then, circle the letter of the choice that best describes the meaning of the underlined suffix as it is used in each pair.

5. heart<u>y</u>   stick<u>y</u>
  (A) belief or practice
  (B) without
  (C) capable of
  (D) characterized by

6. tradition<u>al</u>   music<u>al</u>
  (A) belief or practice of
  (B) unlike
  (C) of, like, suitable for
  (D) without

Word Origins

Directions. Read each of the following sentences. Then, from the vocabulary list below, choose the word that best completes the sentence. Write the word in the blank.

appropriate	cultivate	gorgeous	occasion
assume	disadvantage	hearty	ordinarily
boast	eliminate	import	precipitation
contrast	exert	inviting	quantity
contribute	export	luscious	tradition

7. We get the English word _____ from the Latin word *quantus*, meaning "how great."

8. The English word _____ comes from the Latin word *importare*, meaning "to bring in."

9. We can see the Old French word *gorgias*, meaning "beautiful, glorious," in the English word _____.

10. The English word _____ comes from the Latin noun *occasios*, which means "accidental opportunity" or "fit time."

UNDERSTANDING NEW WORDS AND THEIR USES

Lesson 11 | **CONTEXT:** Ecology and Environment
Writers with a Message

EXERCISE 1 *Multimeaning* ✍

Directions. Read each numbered sentence below. Then, circle the letter of the choice that uses the boldface word in the same way as it is used in the numbered sentence.

1. In Bill Peet's book *Farewell to Shady Glade,* the animals want to preserve their small **plot**.
   (A) A brave rabbit wants to **plot** an attack against the humans' machines.
   (B) The old raccoon says such a **plot** will not work because the machines are too powerful.
   (C) The **plot** of the book revolves around the animals' move to a new Shady Glade.
   (D) You'll be glad to hear that the animals find a safe, new **plot** to call their own.

2. Would it be a **mammoth** task for you to write your own picture book about the environment?
   (A) The main character in your book could be a woolly **mammoth** that arrives in the modern world.
   (B) This animal from the past could view pollution as a **mammoth** problem facing the modern world.
   (C) Perhaps the **mammoth** would want to tackle some polluting companies.
   (D) If you want, you could try drawing your **mammoth** in the style of Dr. Seuss.

EXERCISE 2 *Word Analysis* ✍

Prefixes

Directions. Read each numbered pair of words below. Then, circle the letter of the choice that best describes the meaning of the underlined prefix as it is used in each pair.

3. <u>sub</u>text   <u>sub</u>marine
   (A) beneath
   (B) away from or out of
   (C) above or atop
   (D) less

4. <u>un</u>characteristic   <u>un</u>able
   (A) over
   (B) very
   (C) not
   (D) into

Suffixes

Directions. Read each numbered pair of words below. Then, circle the letter of the choice that best describes the meaning of the underlined suffix as it is used in each pair.

5. inform**ant**   assist**ant**
    (A) one who does
    (B) capable of being
    (C) between
    (D) one who does not

6. visual**ize**   computer**ize**
    (A) make
    (B) not seeing
    (C) do away with
    (D) state of

Word Origins

Directions. Read each of the following sentences. Then, from the vocabulary list below, choose the word that best completes the sentence. Write the word in the blank.

appreciate	doubtless	inspiration	text
braille	entertain	juvenile	theme
campaign	furious	mammoth	urge
characteristic	genuine	plot	visual
conscience	inform	reduction	widespread

7. The Latin word *juvenis,* meaning "young," will help you understand the English word

_____.

8. Two Middle English words, *widen,* meaning "wide," and *spreden,* meaning "spread," were combined to form the word _____.

9. The Greek word *thema,* meaning "what is laid down," has come into the English language as the word _____.

10. The Latin word *conscientia* means "consciousness, moral sense." From it we get the English word _____.

UNDERSTANDING NEW WORDS AND THEIR USES

Lesson 12 | **CONTEXT: Ecology and Environment**
Trash Talk

EXERCISE 1 *Multimeaning*

Directions. Read each numbered sentence below. Then, circle the letter of the choice that uses the boldface word in the same way as it is used in the numbered sentence.

1. Do you get upset when people **foul** the landscape with trash?
   (A) There are many ways to **foul** the environment, and littering is one of them.
   (B) Littering is a **foul** crime.
   (C) My dad picks up litter along our road each Saturday, even in **foul** weather.
   (D) Even a **foul** baseball, when no one claims it, can become garbage.

2. The committee will **issue** the results of its public survey about trash and recycling next week.
   (A) Thank goodness people have started making an **issue** out of garbage!
   (B) In what **issue** of *Newsweek* did you find the newest figures on the amount of trash produced yearly in the world?
   (C) Does the city plan to **issue** new recycling guidelines?
   (D) The mayor called the latest garbage solution "the **issue** of an unimaginative committee."

EXERCISE 2 *Word Analysis*

Prefixes

Directions. Read each numbered pair of words below. Then, circle the letter of the choice that best describes the meaning of the underlined prefix as it is used in each pair.

3. <u>mis</u>guidance   <u>mis</u>fortune
   (A) very
   (B) bad
   (C) previous
   (D) total

4. <u>in</u>expensive   <u>in</u>capable
   (A) not
   (B) extremely
   (C) under
   (D) state of being

Suffixes

Directions. Read each numbered pair of words below. Then, circle the letter of the choice that best describes the meaning of the underlined suffix as it is used in each pair.

5. corporat<u>ion</u>   desperat<u>ion</u>
    (A) not existing
    (B) condition or result of
    (C) quality of
    (D) capable of

6. employ<u>er</u>   destroy<u>er</u>
    (A) full of
    (B) having the quality of
    (C) state of being
    (D) one who or that which

Word Origins

Directions. Read each of the following sentences. Then, from the vocabulary list below, choose the word that best completes the sentence. Write the word in the blank.

adjust	disgust	hazard	protest
applaud	dissolve	inexpensive	remedy
ballot	employer	issue	revolution
candidate	foul	merchandise	temporary
corporation	guidance	persuade	villain

7. The Latin word *villanus,* meaning "farm servant," has changed in spelling and meaning to become the English word _____.

8. It is easy to see the Latin word *applaudere,* meaning "to clap hands," in the English word _____.

9. The Middle French word *desgoust,* meaning "distaste," is similar in spelling to the English word _____.

10. The Latin word *persuadere,* which means "to urge," has come into English as the word _____.

UNDERSTANDING NEW WORDS AND THEIR USES

Lesson 13 **CONTEXT:** Ecology and Environment

A Visit to the Adirondacks

EXERCISE 1 *Multimeaning*

Directions. Read each numbered sentence below. Then, circle the letter of the choice that uses the boldface word in the same way as it is used in the numbered sentence.

1. Having her dogs in her home in the woods gave ecologist Anne LaBastille, the author of *Woodswoman*, a feeling of **security**.
   (A) My mother used her cottage in the Adirondacks as **security** for the loan.
   (B) If you lived in an isolated cabin in the woods, you could not call **security** for protection.
   (C) Knowing that neighbors are close in the woods would give me a sense of **security**.
   (D) Of course, **security** was tight during the 1980 Winter Olympics in the Adirondacks.

2. The **offense** in the battle against polluters in the Adirondacks includes the National Wildlife Federation.
   (A) The author might take **offense** if I said I did not want to be a woodswoman like her.
   (B) During a football game at our family reunion in the Adirondacks, my brothers and I played **offense** against our cousins' defense.
   (C) Destroying forests in the Adirondacks is, of course, a serious **offense**.
   (D) Campers without concern for the environment are an **offense** to environmentalists everywhere.

EXERCISE 2 *Word Analysis*

Prefixes

Directions. Read each numbered pair of words below. Then, circle the letter of the choice that best describes the meaning of the underlined prefix as it is used in each pair.

3. <u>co</u>operate   <u>co</u>pilot
   (A) without
   (B) away from
   (C) with, together
   (D) extra

4. <u>non</u>resident   <u>non</u>believer
   (A) always
   (B) somewhat
   (C) without
   (D) not

Suffixes

Directions. Read each numbered pair of words below. Then, circle the letter of the choice that best describes the meaning of the underlined suffix as it is used in each pair.

5. absorb**able**   market**able**
 (A) act or state of
 (B) capable of being
 (C) not capable of being
 (D) one who

6. amateur**ish**   self**ish**
 (A) not including
 (B) that which belongs to
 (C) unlike
 (D) characterized by

Word Origins

Directions. Read each of the following sentences. Then, from the vocabulary list below, choose the word that best completes the sentence. Write the word in the blank.

absorb	duplicate	omit	security
amateur	intrusion	privacy	self-respect
complaint	keen	rebel	simplify
cooperate	mourning	regret	sympathy
debt	offense	resident	tension

7. From the Latin word *tensio*, meaning "tense," we get the English word

_____.

8. We can easily see the Latin word *privatus*, meaning "belonging to oneself, not the state," in the English word _____.

9. The English word _____ comes from the Latin word *complangere*, meaning "to beat the breast," an action that shows dismay or suffering.

10. The Old English word *cene*, meaning "wise, learned," became the Middle English word *kene* and the Modern English word _____.

UNDERSTANDING NEW WORDS AND THEIR USES

Lesson 14 | CONTEXT: Ecology and Environment
Appreciating the Elephant

EXERCISE 1 · Multimeaning

Directions. Read each numbered sentence below. Then, circle the letter of the choice that uses the boldface word in the same way as it is used in the numbered sentence.

1. A total worldwide ban on the ivory trade would be a **benefit** to elephants.
   - (A) Of course, people who trade in ivory for a living would not **benefit** from such a ban.
   - (B) Tourists who come to see elephants at Kenya's Amboseli National Park are a **benefit** to the country's economy.
   - (C) Many causes can **benefit** from holding a fund-raising event.
   - (D) More than a million dollars was raised at the **benefit** for endangered elephants.

2. Elephants are especially threatened today by a **decrease** in available land for their herds.
   - (A) Elephant herds may **decrease** because they do not have enough land and food.
   - (B) I hope world wildlife agencies do not **decrease** their funds and efforts to save the elephants.
   - (C) The **decrease** in the habitats of both the Indian and African elephants is shocking.
   - (D) My interest in elephant preservation will never **decrease**.

EXERCISE 2 · Word Analysis

Prefixes

Directions. Read each numbered pair of words below. Then, circle the letter of the choice that best describes the meaning of the underlined prefix as it is used in each pair.

3. <u>re</u>unite   <u>re</u>do
   - (A) again
   - (B) not
   - (C) after
   - (D) against

4. <u>un</u>fortunate   <u>un</u>lucky
   - (A) under
   - (B) very
   - (C) not
   - (D) into

Suffixes

Directions. Read each numbered pair of words below. Then, circle the letter of the choice that best describes the meaning of the underlined suffix as it is used in each pair.

5. captiv<u>ity</u>   necess<u>ity</u>
   (A) in
   (B) without
   (C) state of being
   (D) full of

6. surviv<u>al</u>   reviv<u>al</u>
   (A) make
   (B) one who does
   (C) of or relating to
   (D) position of

Word Origins

Directions. Read each of the following sentences. Then, from the vocabulary list below, choose the word that best completes the sentence. Write the word in the blank.

benefit	obvious	resemble	threat
captivity	prey	responsibility	tragedy
decrease	prohibit	severe	unfortunate
eavesdrop	provoke	suburb	unite
migrate	reckless	survival	vocal

7. In Latin, *sub* means "near," and *urb* means "city." Our word for a residential area near a city is _____.

8. The Greek word *tragoidia*, meaning "goat song," has come into the English language as the word _____. It may help to know that it is related to a form of singing in Greek plays.

9. The English word _____ comes from the Latin word *provocare*, meaning "to call forth."

10. The Latin word *severus*, meaning "stern or exacting," has come into English as the word _____.

UNDERSTANDING NEW WORDS AND THEIR USES

Lesson 15 | **CONTEXT:** Ecology and Environment

Chief Seattle: Words for the Wise

EXERCISE 1 *Multimeaning* ✍

Directions. Read each numbered sentence below. Then, circle the letter of the choice that uses the boldface word in the same way as it is used in the numbered sentence.

1. An **associate** of my father's has a book containing many of Chief Seattle's thoughts about "this beautiful land."
   - (A) The new **associate** professor of history knows a lot about this great chief, who led the Suquamish peoples of the Pacific Northwest in the 1800s.
   - (B) It must have been interesting to have been an **associate** of Chief Seattle.
   - (C) Do you **associate** Chief Seattle's name with the city of Seattle?
   - (D) I prefer to **associate** with people who share Chief Seattle's views about the environment.

2. The professor received a **promotion** after finishing his study of Chief Seattle.
   - (A) **Promotion** for the new book about Chief Seattle was especially heavy in Washington.
   - (B) In my opinion, Chief Seattle's views need more **promotion**. If more people were aware of them, our environment might get better protection.
   - (C) In 1962, many people were involved in the **promotion** of a world's fair in Seattle.
   - (D) A friend got a **promotion** at her job for helping design city parks for the fair.

EXERCISE 2 *Word Analysis* ✍

Prefixes

Directions. Read each numbered pair of words below. Then, circle the letter of the choice that best describes the meaning of the underlined prefix as it is used in each pair.

3. <u>im</u>patience   <u>im</u>politeness
   - (A) very
   - (B) over
   - (C) not
   - (D) often

4. <u>re</u>nominate   <u>re</u>run
   - (A) against
   - (B) really
   - (C) never
   - (D) again

Suffixes

Directions. Read each numbered pair of words below. Then, circle the letter of the choice that best describes the meaning of the underlined suffix as it is used in each pair.

5. apolog<u>ize</u>   familiar<u>ize</u>
   (A) without
   (B) to make
   (C) full of
   (D) to take away

6. specific<u>ity</u>   possibil<u>ity</u>
   (A) condition or state of being
   (B) practice, act, or occupation of
   (C) study of
   (D) with, together

Word Origins

Directions. Read each of the following sentences. Then, from the vocabulary list below, choose the word that best completes the sentence. Write the word in the blank.

anthem	courteous	justify	rehearsal
apologize	engage	nominate	reservoir
application	frantic	pollute	specify
associate	hesitate	promotion	superior
compliment	impatience	qualify	toxic

7. We get our English word _____ from the Old French word *engagier*, meaning "to pledge."

8. Our word _____, meaning "a song of praise or loyalty," comes from the Greek word *antiphonos*, meaning "sounding back."

9. We can still see the Latin word *qualificare*, meaning "to attribute a quality to," in the English word _____.

10. The English word _____ comes from the French word *réserver*, meaning "to reserve."

Why We Practice Analogies

Practice with analogies builds logic skills. To answer analogy questions correctly, you think about two words and discover the relationship between them. Then you match that relationship with one shared by another pair of words. In addition, when you study analogies, you think about the precise meanings of words and fix these definitions in your memory.

Understanding Word Analogies

A word analogy is a comparison between two pairs of words. Here is how word analogies are written:

Example 1 FIND : LOCATE :: lose : misplace

The colon (:) stands for the phrase "is related to." Here is how to read the relationships in Example 1:

> FIND [is related to] LOCATE
> lose [is related to] misplace

The double colon [::] between the two pairs of words stands for the phrase "in the same way that." Here is how to read the complete analogy:

> FIND [is related to] LOCATE
> [in the same way that]
> lose [is related to] misplace

Here is another way:

> FIND is to LOCATE as lose is to misplace.

A properly constructed analogy, then, tells us that the relationship between the first pair of words is the same as the relationship between the second pair of words. In Example 1, *find* and *locate* are synonyms, just as *lose* and *misplace* are synonyms.

Let's look at another example:

Example 2 GIFT : JOY :: grief : tears

What is the relationship here? A *gift* causes *joy*, just as *grief* causes *tears*. These two pairs of words have the same relationship, a cause-and-effect relationship. The chart on page 156 will help you to identify analogy relationships. No chart could list all possible relationships between words, but the twelve relationships on the chart are the ones most often used. Also, they are the only relationships used in the analogy lessons.

TYPES OF ANALOGIES		
RELATIONSHIP	**EXAMPLE**	**EXPLANATION**
Synonym	DRY : ARID :: find : locate	*Dry* is similar in meaning to *arid*, just as *find* is similar in meaning to *locate*.
Antonym	KIND : CRUEL :: find : lose	A *kind* action is the opposite of a *cruel* action, just as to *find* something is the opposite of to *lose* it.
Cause and Effect	GIFT : JOY :: rain : flood	A *gift* can cause *joy*, just as *rain* can cause a *flood*.
Part and Whole	CHAPTER : BOOK :: fender : automobile	A *chapter* is a part of a *book*, just as a *fender* is a part of an *automobile*.
Classification	POLKA : DANCE :: frog : amphibian	A *polka* may be classified as a *dance*, just as a *frog* may be classified as an *amphibian*.
Characteristic Quality	PUPPIES : FURRY :: fish : slippery	*Puppies* are *furry*, just as *fish* are *slippery*.
Degree	CHUCKLE : LAUGH :: whimper : cry	A *chuckle* is a little *laugh*, just as a *whimper* is a little *cry*.
Function	KNIFE : CUT :: pen : write	The function of a *knife* is to *cut*, just as the function of a *pen* is to *write*.
Performer and Action	AUTHOR : WRITE :: chef : cook	You expect an *author* to *write*, just as you expect a *chef* to *cook*.
Performer and Object	CASHIER : CASH :: plumber : pipe	A *cashier* works with *cash*, just as a *plumber* works with *pipe*.
Action and Object	BOIL : EGG :: throw : ball	You *boil* an *egg*, just as you *throw* a *ball*.
Location	FISH : SEA :: moose : forest	A *fish* can be found in the *sea*, just as a *moose* can be found in a *forest*.

A Process for Solving Analogies

Your job in solving multiple-choice analogy questions is to identify the relationship between the first two words and then to find the pair of words that has the most similar relationship. Keep in mind that a word pair has the same relationship no matter in which order the two words appear. For example, both CHAPTER : BOOK and BOOK : CHAPTER have a part-and-whole relationship. Here is a hint for identifying relationships. Try using word pairs in the explanation sentences on the chart. When a word pair makes sense in the explanation sentence for a particular relationship, you have found the relationship that the two words have to each other.

Here is a process that will help you with analogy questions:

Answering Analogy Questions: A 4-Step Method

1. Identify the relationship between the capitalized pair of words.
2. Identify the relationship between the pair of words in each possible answer.
3. Eliminate answer choices that have relationships that do not match the relationship between the capitalized words.
4. Choose the remaining possible answer. This answer will have the same relationship as the capitalized pair.

Let's apply this pattern to a sample question.

Example 3

WRITE : PEN :: __F__   [*Function*]

(A) toe : foot _PW_   [*Part and Whole*—does not match]
(B) toss : salad _AO_   [*Action and Object*—does not match]
(C) gymnast : mat _PO_   [*Performer and Object*—does not match]
(D) sky : blue _CQ_   [*Characteristic Quality*—does not match]
(E) shine : sun __F__   [*Function*—does match]

None of relationships (A) through (D) match that of the capitalized pair. They can be eliminated. Choice E must be the correct answer. Notice that the words make sense in the explanation sentence: The function of a *pen* is to *write* just as the function of the *sun* is to *shine*.

A Final Word

Analogies are easier and more fun if you tackle them with a sense of adventure. Allow yourself to discover the relationship between the first pair of words and to explore the relationships between the words in the answer choices. Keep in mind that some words can represent more than one part of speech and that many words have several meanings. Remember, these little verbal puzzles call for flexibility as well as logic.

CONNECTING NEW WORDS AND PATTERNS

Lesson 1 ANALOGIES

Directions. On each line, write the letter or letters that describe the type of relationship the words have to each other. Choose from the following types:

S synonym	A antonym	PW part and whole	PA performer and action
F function	L location	CE cause and effect	PO performer and object
D degree	C classification	CQ characteristic quality	AO action and object

Circle the letter of the pair of words that has the same relationship as the capitalized words. Each relationship is used no more than once in each numbered item.

1. CONFERENCE : MEETING :: ____
   (A) core : apple ____
   (B) people : persons ____
   (C) old : young ____
   (D) firefighter : fire engine ____
   (E) vegetable : garden ____

2. DESCENDANT : ANCESTOR :: ____
   (A) history : past ____
   (B) anger : rage ____
   (C) violinist : violin ____
   (D) cup : handle ____
   (E) inside : outside ____

3. DOUBTFUL : UNSURE :: ____
   (A) detective : investigate ____
   (B) nonfiction : fiction ____
   (C) hurt : harmed ____
   (D) famous : celebrity ____
   (E) whale : ocean ____

4. INNUMERABLE : FEW :: ____
   (A) calm : peaceful ____
   (B) safe : dangerous ____
   (C) long : longer ____
   (D) fork : utensil ____
   (E) juice : sweet ____

5. JOURNALISM : INFORM :: ____
   (A) comedy : amuse ____
   (B) pants : trousers ____
   (C) singer : microphone ____
   (D) crave : eat ____
   (E) musician : pianist ____

6. LEGEND : MYTH :: ____
   (A) page : book ____
   (B) storm : damage ____
   (C) rhythm : beat ____
   (D) upset : calm ____
   (E) author : write ____

7. MAJORITY : MINORITY :: ____
   (A) throw : ball ____
   (B) brim : hat ____
   (C) odd : even ____
   (D) photographer : camera ____
   (E) puddle : wet ____

8. NAVIGATOR : STEER :: ____
   (A) chauffeur : drive ____
   (B) cut : knife ____
   (C) buckle : belt ____
   (D) private : personal ____
   (E) elephant : large ____

9. SYMBOL : FLAG :: ____
   (A) headboard : bed ____
   (B) typhoon : damage ____
   (C) mechanic : wrench ____
   (D) politician : senator ____
   (E) asleep : awake ____

10. VIVID : LIVELY :: ____
   (A) special : ordinary ____
   (B) necessary : needed ____
   (C) shrub : yard ____
   (D) armor : protect ____
   (E) drizzle : downpour ____

CONNECTING NEW WORDS AND PATTERNS

Lesson 2 ANALOGIES

Directions. On each line, write the letter or letters that describe the type of relationship the words have to each other. Choose from the following types:

S synonym A antonym   PW part and whole   PA performer and action
F function L location   CE cause and effect   PO performer and object
D degree   C classification CQ characteristic quality AO action and object

Circle the letter of the pair of words that has the same relationship as the capitalized words. Each relationship is used no more than once in each numbered item.

1. AVIATION : SCIENCE :: ____
   (A) plant : sow ____
   (B) minerals : earth ____
   (C) typing : skill ____
   (D) handlebar : bike ____
   (E) circle : round ____

2. COLLIDE : CRASH :: ____
   (A) toss : hurl ____
   (B) face : clock ____
   (C) diet : weight loss ____
   (D) painter : paintbrush ____
   (E) break : repair ____

3. COMPLEX : INVOLVED :: ____
   (A) steel : hard ____
   (B) grow : shrink ____
   (C) glance : peek ____
   (D) English : language ____
   (E) overspending : debt ____

4. DEPARTURE : ARRIVAL :: ____
   (A) teacher : textbook ____
   (B) sip : juice ____
   (C) left : right ____
   (D) joke : laughter ____
   (E) book : shelf ____

5. DISTURB : BOTHER :: ____
   (A) show : display ____
   (B) write : erase ____
   (C) shoes : protect ____
   (D) deer : forest ____
   (E) flannel : fabric ____

6. FATAL : HARMFUL :: ____
   (A) dictionary : book ____
   (B) clouds : sky ____
   (C) brilliant : bright ____
   (D) secretary : computer ____
   (E) heel : boot ____

7. FOUNDATION : STRUCTURE :: ____
   (A) addition : subtraction ____
   (B) yardstick : measure ____
   (C) opera : opera house ____
   (D) introduction : essay ____
   (E) whale : large ____

8. INCIDENT : EVENT :: ____
   (A) employer : hire ____
   (B) car : automobile ____
   (C) piano : instrument ____
   (D) range : mountain ____
   (E) farmer : tractor ____

9. NUISANCE : ANNOYING :: ____
   (A) gull : beach ____
   (B) medical bag : doctor ____
   (C) collar : jacket ____
   (D) riddle : puzzling ____
   (E) bull : animal ____

10. RASH : CAREFUL :: ____
    (A) goodness : praise ____
    (B) troublesome : difficult ____
    (C) messy : neat ____
    (D) wash : dishes ____
    (E) red : color ____

CONNECTING NEW WORDS AND PATTERNS

Lesson 3 ANALOGIES

Directions. On each line, write the letter or letters that describe the type of relationship the words have to each other. Choose from the following types:

S synonym	A antonym	PW part and whole	PA performer and action
F function	L location	CE cause and effect	PO performer and object
D degree	C classification	CQ characteristic quality	AO action and object

Circle the letter of the pair of words that has the same relationship as the capitalized words. Each relationship is used no more than once in each numbered item.

1. ABDOMEN : BODY :: _____
   (A) trunk : elephant _____
   (B) furry : rabbit _____
   (C) empty : vacant _____
   (D) stressed : relaxed _____
   (E) cook : boil _____

2. CAUTION : CARELESSNESS :: _____
   (A) movement : motion _____
   (B) sprinkle : pour _____
   (C) sound : silence _____
   (D) fire : hot _____
   (E) noun : grammar _____

3. COMMOTION : DISTURBANCE :: _____
   (A) person : crowd _____
   (B) rapid : slow _____
   (C) value : worth _____
   (D) work : pay _____
   (E) scissors : cut _____

4. FLEXIBLE : RUBBER :: _____
   (A) uprising : revolt _____
   (B) fragrant : perfume _____
   (C) nervous : calm _____
   (D) boredom : yawn _____
   (E) nurse : thermometer _____

5. FOE : FRIEND :: _____
   (A) banker : loan _____
   (B) player : team _____
   (C) beginning : conclusion _____
   (D) broccoli : vegetable _____
   (E) wash : scour _____

6. GRATITUDE : FAVOR :: _____
   (A) chess : game _____
   (B) salt : saltshaker _____
   (C) anger : insult _____
   (D) legs : table _____
   (E) salesperson : sell _____

7. HEROIC : RESCUER :: _____
   (A) honest : truthful _____
   (B) musician : oboe _____
   (C) photographer : shoot _____
   (D) teeth : bite _____
   (E) royal : prince _____

8. HOIST : CRANE :: _____
   (A) east : direction _____
   (B) transport : truck _____
   (C) compass needle : magnetic _____
   (D) inquire : ask _____
   (E) pass : fail _____

9. MAXIMUM : GREATEST :: _____
   (A) least : smallest _____
   (B) cool : freezing _____
   (C) close : door _____
   (D) star : bright _____
   (E) funniest : saddest _____

10. PREVIOUS : NEXT :: _____
    (A) student : notebook _____
    (B) suggest : insist _____
    (C) rushing : clumsiness _____
    (D) certain : sure _____
    (E) boring : entertaining _____

CONNECTING NEW WORDS AND PATTERNS

Lesson 4   ANALOGIES

Directions. On each line, write the letter or letters that describe the type of relationship the words have to each other. Choose from the following types:

S synonym   A antonym   PW part and whole   PA performer and action
F function   L location   CE cause and effect   PO performer and object
D degree   C classification   CQ characteristic quality   AO action and object

Circle the letter of the pair of words that has the same relationship as the capitalized words. Each relationship is used no more than once in each numbered item.

1. ACQUIRE : GET :: _____
   (A) instrument : clarinet _____
   (B) repair : improvement _____
   (C) knob : television _____
   (D) celebrate : grieve _____
   (E) wish : desire _____

2. DAINTY : LACE :: _____
   (A) open : close _____
   (B) swift : fast _____
   (C) tablecloth : cover _____
   (D) waiter : restaurant _____
   (E) sparkling : diamond _____

3. DISGUISE : EXPOSE :: _____
   (A) bore : entertain _____
   (B) location : place _____
   (C) driver : truck _____
   (D) search : find _____
   (E) chef : bake _____

4. EARNEST : JOKING :: _____
   (A) sadness : emotion _____
   (B) exercise : sweat _____
   (C) steady : regular _____
   (D) pretty : beautiful _____
   (E) noisy : quiet _____

5. GASP : SURPRISE :: _____
   (A) short : tall _____
   (B) trot : gallop _____
   (C) happiness : emotion _____
   (D) tears : sorrow _____
   (E) tour : journey _____

6. HIBERNATE : BEAR :: _____
   (A) scissors : cut _____
   (B) method : system _____
   (C) injury : pain _____
   (D) hurt : heal _____
   (E) travel : tourist _____

7. INHALE : AIR :: _____
   (A) farmer : silo _____
   (B) maple : tree _____
   (C) surprised : shocked _____
   (D) rake : leaves _____
   (E) rubber band : stretchy _____

8. LINGER : WAIT :: _____
   (A) sneeze : dust _____
   (B) talk : chat _____
   (C) play : work _____
   (D) gymnast : tumble _____
   (E) tiger : meat eating _____

9. REQUIREMENT : NECESSITY :: _____
   (A) help : assistance _____
   (B) boat : ocean _____
   (C) arrive : depart _____
   (D) waiter : menu _____
   (E) game : fun _____

10. VACUUM : EMPTY :: _____
   (A) jumble : mess _____
   (B) North America : continent _____
   (C) lightning : bright _____
   (D) finger : hand _____
   (E) mirror : reflect _____

CONNECTING NEW WORDS AND PATTERNS

Lesson 5 | ANALOGIES

Directions. On each line, write the letter or letters that describe the type of relationship the words have to each other. Choose from the following types:

S synonym	A antonym	PW part and whole	PA performer and action
F function	L location	CE cause and effect	PO performer and object
D degree	C classification	CQ characteristic quality	AO action and object

Circle the letter of the pair of words that has the same relationship as the capitalized words. Each relationship is used no more than once in each numbered item.

1. BUREAU : AGENCY :: _____
(A) divide : multiply _____
(B) piece : section _____
(C) sofa : living room _____
(D) arm : chair _____
(E) bed : furniture _____

2. FLAMMABLE : GASOLINE :: _____
(A) asleep : awake _____
(B) ginger : spice _____
(C) notebook : binder _____
(D) startle : terrify _____
(E) absorbent : cotton _____

3. JEOPARDY : RISK :: _____
(A) spill : stain _____
(B) strange : unfamiliar _____
(C) cuff : pants _____
(D) pitcher : ball _____
(E) democracy : government _____

4. LUNAR : MOONLIKE :: _____
(A) candidate : speech _____
(B) truth : lie _____
(C) sunny : bright _____
(D) warm : boiling _____
(E) oven : bake _____

5. PHARMACY : MEDICINES :: _____
(A) pretzel : salty _____
(B) tailor : needle _____
(C) kitchen : spices _____
(D) notes : music _____
(E) wild : tame _____

6. PIERCE : HOLE :: _____
(A) wet : dry _____
(B) shoot : target _____
(C) dew : dampness _____
(D) build : carpenter _____
(E) fan : cool _____

7. PRY : CROWBAR :: _____
(A) shave : razor _____
(B) quilt : stitched _____
(C) split : divide _____
(D) pound : nail _____
(E) guitar : instrument _____

8. RESIGN : APPLY :: _____
(A) flood : damage _____
(B) ask : beg _____
(C) divide : combine _____
(D) snow : cold _____
(E) apple : orchard _____

9. STATIC : STATUE :: _____
(A) face : watch _____
(B) easygoing : strict _____
(C) salty : ocean _____
(D) poem : literature _____
(E) nose : smell _____

10. SUSPICION : TRUST :: _____
(A) boredom : interest _____
(B) musician : orchestra _____
(C) autumn : fall _____
(D) glue : sticky _____
(E) book : library _____

CONNECTING NEW WORDS AND PATTERNS

Lesson 6. ANALOGIES

Directions. On each line, write the letter or letters that describe the type of relationship the words have to each other. Choose from the following types:

S synonym	A antonym	PW part and whole	PA performer and action
F function	L location	CE cause and effect	PO performer and object
D degree	C classification	CQ characteristic quality	AO action and object

Circle the letter of the pair of words that has the same relationship as the capitalized words. Each relationship is used no more than once in each numbered item.

1. BIOGRAPHY : NONFICTION :: ____
    (A) smooth : bumpy ____
    (B) able : talented ____
    (C) cement : strong ____
    (D) biology : science ____
    (E) free : independent ____

2. DEBATE : ARGUE :: ____
    (A) select : choose ____
    (B) language : Spanish ____
    (C) encourage : prevent ____
    (D) pit : peach ____
    (E) director : movie ____

3. DOCUMENT :
    BIRTH CERTIFICATE :: ____
    (A) coin : toss ____
    (B) pig : fat ____
    (C) soaked : damp ____
    (D) dependable : reliable ____
    (E) book : dictionary ____

4. ESSENTIAL : UNNECESSARY :: ____
    (A) constant : uninterrupted ____
    (B) cushions : sofa ____
    (C) grinning : frowning ____
    (D) study : learn ____
    (E) ruler : measure ____

5. GENEROUS : STINGY :: ____
    (A) tent : campground ____
    (B) fuzzy : blurry ____
    (C) anger : emotion ____
    (D) rude : polite ____
    (E) observer : binoculars ____

6. IDENTICAL : SIMILAR :: ____
    (A) writer : pencil ____
    (B) mayor : city hall ____
    (C) smart : intelligent ____
    (D) peak : valley ____
    (E) boiling : warm ____

7. PROFESSION : TEACHING :: ____
    (A) sheriff : arrest ____
    (B) speak : talk ____
    (C) want : crave ____
    (D) coaching : improvement ____
    (E) fabric : silk ____

8. ROUTINE : UNUSUAL :: ____
    (A) edge : rim ____
    (B) animal : dog ____
    (C) planned : unexpected ____
    (D) rules : order ____
    (E) pen pal : letter ____

9. SCHOLAR : READ :: ____
    (A) book : index ____
    (B) police officer : badge ____
    (C) mat : gymnasium ____
    (D) tell : say ____
    (E) pilot : fly ____

10. THOROUGH : COMPLETE :: ____
    (A) preparation : readiness ____
    (B) snow : cold ____
    (C) salad : toss ____
    (D) broad : wide ____
    (E) deep : shallow ____

CONNECTING NEW WORDS AND PATTERNS

*L*esson 7 ANALOGIES

Directions. On each line, write the letter or letters that describe the type of relationship the words have to each other. Choose from the following types:

S synonym	**A** antonym	**PW** part and whole	**PA** performer and action
F function	**L** location	**CE** cause and effect	**PO** performer and object
D degree	**C** classification	**CQ** characteristic quality	**AO** action and object

Circle the letter of the pair of words that has the same relationship as the capitalized words. Each relationship is used no more than once in each numbered item.

1. ARCHITECT : BLUEPRINT :: _____
   (A) idle : busy _____
   (B) house : building _____
   (C) composer : symphony _____
   (D) staples : join _____
   (E) build : construct _____

2. BETRAY : DECEIVE :: _____
   (A) tight : loose _____
   (B) work : labor _____
   (C) autumn : season _____
   (D) dock : lake _____
   (E) sculptor : statue _____

3. CEREMONY : WEDDING :: _____
   (A) jog : run _____
   (B) beat : defeat _____
   (C) tug : push _____
   (D) state : Utah _____
   (E) honey : sweet _____

4. DISTRICT : SECTION :: _____
   (A) boring : dull _____
   (B) triangle : shape _____
   (C) cut : bleeding _____
   (D) hockey player : puck _____
   (E) elephants : zoo _____

5. ETERNAL : TEMPORARY :: _____
   (A) powerful : strong _____
   (B) raw : cooked _____
   (C) gills : fish _____
   (D) quartz : rock _____
   (E) pepper : hot _____

6. FRAGRANT : ROSE :: _____
   (A) pirate : steal _____
   (B) fragile : china _____
   (C) lumber : sawmill _____
   (D) petal : flower _____
   (E) lumberjack : timber _____

7. IGNITE : PUT OUT :: _____
   (A) rest : activity _____
   (B) persuade : advertisement _____
   (C) dusk : darkness _____
   (D) carelessness : accident _____
   (E) eat : food _____

8. QUARANTINE : ISOLATION :: _____
   (A) wash : clothes _____
   (B) halt : continue _____
   (C) command : order _____
   (D) liar : dishonest _____
   (E) crime : punishment _____

9. SCHEME : PLOT :: _____
   (A) maps : direct _____
   (B) private : public _____
   (C) sand : beach _____
   (D) order : arrange _____
   (E) brush : hair _____

10. VICTIM : SUFFER :: _____
    (A) folktale : story _____
    (B) water : wet _____
    (C) arrive : leave _____
    (D) victor : win _____
    (E) lawyer : courtroom _____

CONNECTING NEW WORDS AND PATTERNS

Lesson 8 ANALOGIES

Directions. On each line, write the letter or letters that describe the type of relationship the words have to each other. Choose from the following types:

S synonym	A antonym	PW part and whole	PA performer and action
F function	L location	CE cause and effect	PO performer and object
D degree	C classification	CQ characteristic quality	AO action and object

Circle the letter of the pair of words that has the same relationship as the capitalized words. Each relationship is used no more than once in each numbered item.

1. ABUNDANT : PLENTIFUL :: _____
   (A) sour : lemon _____
   (B) rich : wealthy _____
   (C) sharp : blunt _____
   (D) chicken : poultry _____
   (E) mail carrier : letter _____

2. DESCRIPTIVE : DETAILED :: _____
   (A) helpful : hurtful _____
   (B) still : motionless _____
   (C) destructive : war _____
   (D) bumper : car _____
   (E) teacher : chalk _____

3. DESIRABLE : DISGUSTING :: _____
   (A) bright : faded _____
   (B) clean : tidy _____
   (C) pane : window _____
   (D) wash : hair _____
   (E) dirty : filthy _____

4. DRAMATIC : DULL :: _____
   (A) comical : gloomy _____
   (B) magical : enchanting _____
   (C) grass : green _____
   (D) trial : courthouse _____
   (E) song : words _____

5. EXTRAORDINARY : UNUSUAL :: _____
   (A) baby : innocent _____
   (B) feet : walk _____
   (C) awful : bad _____
   (D) buy : sell _____
   (E) children : nursery _____

6. FLOURISH : DISPLAY :: _____
   (A) waltz : dance _____
   (B) vulture : fly _____
   (C) accept : deny _____
   (D) unselfish : generous _____
   (E) stem : apple _____

7. POSSESS : HAVE :: _____
   (A) lift : raise _____
   (B) steal : thief _____
   (C) give : receive _____
   (D) load : camera _____
   (E) book : library _____

8. PREHISTORIC : ANCIENT :: _____
   (A) fishing pole : cast _____
   (B) explorer : travel _____
   (C) poison ivy : itch _____
   (D) screen : computer _____
   (E) yell : shout _____

9. SATISFY : DISAPPOINT :: _____
   (A) mapmaker : draw _____
   (B) laces : shoe _____
   (C) gift : pleasure _____
   (D) approve : reject _____
   (E) reduce : lessen _____

10. TERRAIN : GROUND :: _____
    (A) dirt : plant _____
    (B) answer : ask _____
    (C) ask : request _____
    (D) iron : hard _____
    (E) seed : sprout _____

CONNECTING NEW WORDS AND PATTERNS

Lesson 9 | ANALOGIES

Directions. On each line, write the letter or letters that describe the type of relationship the words have to each other. Choose from the following types:

S synonym   A antonym   PW part and whole   PA performer and action
F function   L location   CE cause and effect   PO performer and object
D degree   C classification   CQ characteristic quality   AO action and object

Circle the letter of the pair of words that has the same relationship as the capitalized words. Each relationship is used no more than once in each numbered item.

1. AMBITIOUS : CONTENT :: _____
   (A) quick : rapid _____
   (B) Earth : planet _____
   (C) large : small _____
   (D) furnace : heat _____
   (E) leaf : green _____

2. ARID : WET :: _____
   (A) slice : knife _____
   (B) hoofed : horse _____
   (C) nightmare : terror _____
   (D) jockey : ride _____
   (E) asleep : awake _____

3. COUNTERFEIT : FAKE :: _____
   (A) plain : fancy _____
   (B) rain : flood _____
   (C) money : buy _____
   (D) banana : sweet _____
   (E) difficult : hard _____

4. ENVY : JEALOUSY :: _____
   (A) hospital : medicine _____
   (B) roof : building _____
   (C) desire : want _____
   (D) chef : pot _____
   (E) artificial : natural _____

5. EXCLAIM : SAY :: _____
   (A) rent : apartment _____
   (B) inspect : glance _____
   (C) poet : imaginative _____
   (D) inner : outer _____
   (E) spark : fire _____

6. ORNAMENTAL : SHRUB :: _____
   (A) igloo : home _____
   (B) write : word processor _____
   (C) money : bank _____
   (D) useful : tool _____
   (E) leave : arrive _____

7. REIGN : KING :: _____
   (A) flower : carnation _____
   (B) door : knob _____
   (C) pasture : cattle _____
   (D) serve : waiter _____
   (E) seedling : tree _____

8. SOLITARY : LONER :: _____
   (A) Boston : city _____
   (B) fussy : agreeable _____
   (C) similar : alike _____
   (D) burner : stove _____
   (E) graceful : dancer _____

9. TRANSPARENT : GLASS :: _____
   (A) breakable : window _____
   (B) foggy : clear _____
   (C) carve : miniature _____
   (D) strings : guitar _____
   (E) cold : shiver _____

10. WARDROBE : OUTFIT :: _____
    (A) rider : horse _____
    (B) refrigerator : chill _____
    (C) tool set : wrench _____
    (D) water : wet _____
    (E) tiny : huge _____

CONNECTING NEW WORDS AND PATTERNS

Lesson 10 ANALOGIES

Directions. On each line, write the letter or letters that describe the type of relationship the words have to each other. Choose from the following types:

S synonym A antonym PW part and whole PA performer and action
F function L location CE cause and effect PO performer and object
D degree C classification CQ characteristic quality AO action and object

Circle the letter of the pair of words that has the same relationship as the capitalized words. Each relationship is used no more than once in each numbered item.

1. APPROPRIATE : UNSUITABLE :: _____
   (A) disappearance : search _____
   (B) valuable : gem _____
   (C) fresh : stale _____
   (D) helpful : useful _____
   (E) teeth : comb _____

2. BOAST : BRAG :: _____
   (A) try : attempt _____
   (B) accept : refuse _____
   (C) joke : giggle _____
   (D) bubble : fragile _____
   (E) beat : drum _____

3. CULTIVATE : GARDEN :: _____
   (A) shock : scream _____
   (B) feed : starve _____
   (C) food : refrigerator _____
   (D) harvest : crop _____
   (E) clown : amuse _____

4. ELIMINATE : INCLUDE :: _____
   (A) start : finish _____
   (B) pear : fruit _____
   (C) copy : duplicate _____
   (D) eat : banana _____
   (E) swings : playground _____

5. EXPORT : GOODS :: _____
   (A) make : create _____
   (B) squeeze : hold _____
   (C) wildflowers : field _____
   (D) write : letter _____
   (E) traveler : map _____

6. INVITING : ATTRACTIVE :: _____
   (A) funny : serious _____
   (B) orange : juicy _____
   (C) librarian : book _____
   (D) gossip : embarrassment _____
   (E) incorrect : wrong _____

7. OCCASION : BIRTHDAY :: _____
   (A) quantity : amount _____
   (B) kingdom : ruler _____
   (C) quilt : bed _____
   (D) athlete : compete _____
   (E) book : dictionary _____

8. ORDINARILY : USUALLY :: _____
   (A) carton : contain _____
   (B) quickly : fast _____
   (C) newspaper : column _____
   (D) accident : injury _____
   (E) car : garage _____

9. PRECIPITATION : SNOW :: _____
   (A) doll : toyshop _____
   (B) marry : wed _____
   (C) sport : golf _____
   (D) hire : fire _____
   (E) strum : guitar _____

10. TRADITION : CUSTOM :: _____
   (A) clock : hands _____
   (B) filth : dirt _____
   (C) summer : warm _____
   (D) egg : hatch _____
   (E) gasoline : gas station _____

CONNECTING NEW WORDS AND PATTERNS

Lesson 11 | ANALOGIES

Directions. On each line, write the letter or letters that describe the type of relationship the words have to each other. Choose from the following types:

S synonym	A antonym	PW part and whole	PA performer and action
F function	L location	CE cause and effect	PO performer and object
D degree	C classification	CQ characteristic quality	AO action and object

Circle the letter of the pair of words that has the same relationship as the capitalized words. Each relationship is used no more than once in each numbered item.

1. APPRECIATE : DESPISE :: _____
   (A) dog : fetch _____
   (B) interest : bore _____
   (C) question : test _____
   (D) whole : entire _____
   (E) monkey : animal _____

2. BRAILLE : READ :: _____
   (A) valley : hill _____
   (B) tiny : small _____
   (C) bracelet : jewelry _____
   (D) cackle : hen _____
   (E) essay : write _____

3. CAMPAIGN : POLITICIAN :: _____
   (A) dime : shiny _____
   (B) board : chess set _____
   (C) swamp : desert _____
   (D) compete : athlete _____
   (E) cab : taxi _____

4. CONSCIENCE : GUIDE :: _____
   (A) brain : think _____
   (B) hunger : eat _____
   (C) bedroom : apartment _____
   (D) mail carrier : pouch _____
   (E) ice : cold _____

5. ENTERTAIN : PERFORMER :: _____
   (A) needy : independent _____
   (B) oven : bake _____
   (C) write : author _____
   (D) strap : backpack _____
   (E) scene : view _____

6. FURIOUS : ANNOYED :: _____
   (A) head : scalp _____
   (B) delighted : glad _____
   (C) break : repair _____
   (D) wear : hat _____
   (E) desert : oasis _____

7. GENUINE : REAL :: _____
   (A) push : grab _____
   (B) magician : perform _____
   (C) rake : leaves _____
   (D) solo : alone _____
   (E) space : rocket _____

8. JUVENILE : MATURE :: _____
   (A) combined : separate _____
   (B) ill : dying _____
   (C) varied : different _____
   (D) infant : crib _____
   (E) close : gate _____

9. THEME : SUBJECT :: _____
   (A) open : close _____
   (B) feather : bird _____
   (C) habit : custom _____
   (D) climb : ladder _____
   (E) chair : furniture _____

10. URGE : SUGGEST :: _____
    (A) mix : blender _____
    (B) slip : fall _____
    (C) crash : bump _____
    (D) mail : letter _____
    (E) hold : drop _____

CONNECTING NEW WORDS AND PATTERNS

Lesson 12 ANALOGIES

Directions. On each line, write the letter or letters that describe the type of relationship the words have to each other. Choose from the following types:

S synonym   A antonym   PW part and whole   PA performer and action
F function   L location   CE cause and effect   PO performer and object
D degree   C classification CQ characteristic quality   AO action and object

Circle the letter of the pair of words that has the same relationship as the capitalized words. Each relationship is used no more than once in each numbered item.

1. BALLOT : VOTER :: _____
   (A) cottage : door _____
   (B) kangaroo : Australia _____
   (C) newspaper : throw _____
   (D) order form : customer _____
   (E) tight : stretched _____

2. DISSOLVE : MELT :: _____
   (A) student : read _____
   (B) wash : cleanse _____
   (C) penny : coin _____
   (D) barber : razor _____
   (E) bee : busy _____

3. GUIDANCE : ADVICE :: _____
   (A) penalty : punishment _____
   (B) teacher : exam _____
   (C) freeze : boil _____
   (D) violin : string _____
   (E) piano : play _____

4. HAZARD : DANGER :: _____
   (A) chance : opportunity _____
   (B) animal : rabbit _____
   (C) drama : perform _____
   (D) shouting : attention _____
   (E) warm : cool _____

5. INEXPENSIVE : COSTLY :: _____
   (A) lawyer : professional _____
   (B) wild : untamed _____
   (C) dressy : casual _____
   (D) ice cream : cold _____
   (E) room : straighten _____

6. MERCHANDISE : MALL :: _____
   (A) grocer : fruit _____
   (B) bread : baked _____
   (C) snout : bear _____
   (D) groceries : supermarket _____
   (E) drama : literature _____

7. PROTEST : AGREE :: _____
   (A) raise : lower _____
   (B) skyscraper : building _____
   (C) memorize : speech _____
   (D) street : paved _____
   (E) wound : pain _____

8. REMEDY : CURE :: _____
   (A) scorching : freezing _____
   (B) memory : recollection _____
   (C) race : exciting _____
   (D) tower : castle _____
   (E) planet : Saturn _____

9. REVOLUTION : REVOLT :: _____
   (A) author : revise _____
   (B) limousine : driver _____
   (C) election : select _____
   (D) street : avenue _____
   (E) contest : enter _____

10. TEMPORARY : PERMANENT :: _____
   (A) calm : upset _____
   (B) test : final exam _____
   (C) fur : soft _____
   (D) mountain : hill _____
   (E) first : earliest _____

CONNECTING NEW WORDS AND PATTERNS

Lesson 13 ANALOGIES

Directions. On each line, write the letter or letters that describe the type of relationship the words have to each other. Choose from the following types:

S synonym	A antonym	PW part and whole	PA performer and action
F function	L location	CE cause and effect	PO performer and object
D degree	C classification	CQ characteristic quality	AO action and object

Circle the letter of the pair of words that has the same relationship as the capitalized words. Each relationship is used no more than once in each numbered item.

1. AMATEUR : PROFESSIONAL :: _____
   (A) healthy : fit _____
   (B) mechanic : wrench _____
   (C) plum : fruit _____
   (D) loud : bagpipe _____
   (E) neat : disorderly _____

2. COMPLAINT : PROBLEM :: _____
   (A) food : nourishing _____
   (B) umbrella : protect _____
   (C) praise : success _____
   (D) coffee : brew _____
   (E) sport : hockey _____

3. DEBT : PAY OFF :: _____
   (A) jeweler : gem _____
   (B) sky : cloud _____
   (C) rocks : stones _____
   (D) April : month _____
   (E) law : obey _____

4. DUPLICATE : COPY :: _____
   (A) ax : chop _____
   (B) baker : pie _____
   (C) position : location _____
   (D) question : test _____
   (E) polar bear : white _____

5. MOURNING : DEATH :: _____
   (A) celebration : victory _____
   (B) bear : den _____
   (C) sip : milk _____
   (D) summer : season _____
   (E) hummingbird : fly _____

6. OMIT : INCLUDE :: _____
   (A) statesman : lead _____
   (B) recover : improve _____
   (C) trunk : tree _____
   (D) collect : taxes _____
   (E) pay : borrow _____

7. REBEL : OBEY :: _____
   (A) scare : frighten _____
   (B) bore : entertain _____
   (C) sheriff : protect _____
   (D) wing : airplane _____
   (E) president : Lincoln _____

8. REGRET : FEELING :: _____
   (A) refrigerator : kitchen _____
   (B) bubble : pop _____
   (C) pleasantness : attitude _____
   (D) bear : growl _____
   (E) oil : slippery _____

9. SELF-RESPECT : SELF-ESTEEM :: _____
   (A) France : nation _____
   (B) faith : belief _____
   (C) word : sentence _____
   (D) reward : punish _____
   (E) magazine : read _____

10. SYMPATHY : PITY :: _____
    (A) entrance : exit _____
    (B) springtime : breezy _____
    (C) cards : shuffle _____
    (D) robbery : theft _____
    (E) dog : pet _____

CONNECTING NEW WORDS AND PATTERNS

Lesson 14 | ANALOGIES

Directions. On each line, write the letter or letters that describe the type of relationship the words have to each other. Choose from the following types:

S synonym   A antonym   PW part and whole   PA performer and action
F function   L location   CE cause and effect   PO performer and object
D degree   C classification CQ characteristic quality AO action and object

Circle the letter of the pair of words that has the same relationship as the capitalized words. Each relationship is used no more than once in each numbered item.

1. OBVIOUS : HIDDEN :: ____
   (A) scarce : rare ____
   (B) tired : exhausted ____
   (C) soap : clean ____
   (D) completed : unfinished ____
   (E) candle : burn ____

2. PREY : HUNTED :: ____
   (A) eyes : see ____
   (B) door : slam ____
   (C) tornado : damage ____
   (D) nail : hardware ____
   (E) artist : inspired ____

3. PROHIBIT : ALLOW :: ____
   (A) teacher : chalk ____
   (B) water : liquid ____
   (C) throw : toss ____
   (D) defend : attack ____
   (E) gardener : trim ____

4. RECKLESS : CAREFUL :: ____
   (A) clumsy : graceful ____
   (B) sister : relative ____
   (C) fish : aquarium ____
   (D) overdue : late ____
   (E) damage : destroy ____

5. RESEMBLE : MATCH :: ____
   (A) flowers : garden ____
   (B) motorcycle : seat ____
   (C) globe : round ____
   (D) suggest : demand ____
   (E) load : film ____

6. RESPONSIBILITY : DUTY :: ____
   (A) robin : bird ____
   (B) firefighter : ladder ____
   (C) job : occupation ____
   (D) life : death ____
   (E) smoke : hazy ____

7. SUBURBS : OUTSKIRTS :: ____
   (A) speed : danger ____
   (B) areas : sections ____
   (C) coin : quarter ____
   (D) menu : restaurant ____
   (E) wagon : carry ____

8. TRAGEDY : SUFFERING :: ____
   (A) lens : camera ____
   (B) glance : stare ____
   (C) necklace : jewelry ____
   (D) delay : tardiness ____
   (E) ride : bike ____

9. UNITE : DIVIDE :: ____
   (A) work : loaf ____
   (B) collie : dog ____
   (C) cowboy : stirrup ____
   (D) squirrel : tree ____
   (E) flowers : arrange ____

10. VOCAL : PARROT :: ____
    (A) teeth : bite ____
    (B) dangerous : hazardous ____
    (C) quiet : library ____
    (D) green : color ____
    (E) cave : bats ____

CONNECTING NEW WORDS AND PATTERNS

Lesson 15 | ANALOGIES

Directions. On each line, write the letter or letters that describe the type of relationship the words have to each other. Choose from the following types:

S synonym	A antonym	PW part and whole	PA performer and action
F function	L location	CE cause and effect	PO performer and object
D degree	C classification	CQ characteristic quality	AO action and object

Circle the letter of the pair of words that has the same relationship as the capitalized words. Each relationship is used no more than once in each numbered item.

1. COMPLIMENT : INSULT :: _____
   (A) critic : movie review _____
   (B) singer : perform _____
   (C) eagle : bird _____
   (D) hate : detest _____
   (E) disappoint : please _____

2. COURTEOUS : IMPOLITE :: _____
   (A) swimmer : swim _____
   (B) quick : rabbit _____
   (C) expensive : cheap _____
   (D) lawful : legal _____
   (E) biology : science _____

3. FRANTIC : UPSET :: _____
   (A) wild : lively _____
   (B) scoreboard : gym _____
   (C) jazz : music _____
   (D) push : pull _____
   (E) poet : write _____

4. HESITATE : PAUSE :: _____
   (A) walk : stroll _____
   (B) wax : candle _____
   (C) shark : ocean _____
   (D) tree : oak _____
   (E) pass : fail _____

5. IMPATIENCE : DELAYS :: _____
   (A) take : grab _____
   (B) athlete : train _____
   (C) thirst : dryness _____
   (D) path : trail _____
   (E) ship : mast _____

6. POLLUTE : MIND :: _____
   (A) laugh : cry _____
   (B) praise : flatter _____
   (C) contest : rules _____
   (D) explanation : understanding _____
   (E) paint : picture _____

7. REHEARSAL : DRILL :: _____
   (A) horrible : wonderful _____
   (B) tune : melody _____
   (C) doorbell : push _____
   (D) towel : dry _____
   (E) attic : house _____

8. RESERVOIR : STORE :: _____
   (A) point : direct _____
   (B) flexible : stubborn _____
   (C) guest : arrive _____
   (D) worship : admire _____
   (E) paper clip : join _____

9. SUPERIOR : AVERAGE :: _____
   (A) strike : match _____
   (B) parent : nurture _____
   (C) pumpkin : orange _____
   (D) dog : pet _____
   (E) love : like _____

10. TOXIC : PURE :: _____
    (A) shark : fin _____
    (B) clever : tricky _____
    (C) round : ball _____
    (D) difficult : easy _____
    (E) bicyclist : helmet _____

Why We Read Strategically

Reading is active. As you read, you step into the writer's world. When you come across a new idea, you usually look for a clue to help you determine the writer's meaning. You move ahead to see if the idea is explained, or you retrace your steps to look for any signs you missed.

You can use these same strategies to build your vocabulary. If you do not know the meaning of a word, you should look in the passage surrounding the word for hints. These hints are called context clues. The more you practice hunting for context clues, the better you become at reading new words, and the larger your vocabulary will grow. Remember, strengthening your vocabulary skills will help you to score higher on standardized vocabulary tests.

The following reading selection shows the kinds of context clues you will find in the Reading New Words in Context lessons.

Strategic Reading: An Example

Long, long ago, long before there were humans on Earth—much less humans who could record history—dinosaurs walked the earth. During these **prehistoric** times, strange and wonderful creatures ruled the entire earth. All in all, *this* **reign** lasted 135 million years.

The dinosaur was one **descendant** of the thecodonts, mighty reptiles whose *later generations* also included many other reptiles, as well as all of today's birds. One of these relatives was a huge flying reptile. Another was a creature with a body like that of a turtle but with a 25-foot-long neck. Like the dinosaurs, these unusual *and* **extraordinary** creatures became extinct. Any of these creatures has the power to *stun,* **astonish,** *and amaze* us, but it is the dinosaurs that most people find especially fascinating.

Some dinosaurs were **mammoth** creatures. *The euhelopus, for example, was 60 feet tall and weighed 50,000 pounds.* In contrast, the 20-foot, 7,000-pound stegosaurus seems almost small. Although enormous size *was* a **characteristic** of many dinosaurs, others were much, much smaller, no bigger than a chicken or a duck. Some of these smaller ones looked much like either the iguana or the komodo dragon, two reptiles that inhabit Earth today.

Note that a *summary* indicates the meaning of **prehistoric**.

A *pronoun* (*this*) refers us to the meaning of **reign**.
The meaning of **descendant** is made clear through *restatement,* that is, through saying the same thing in a different way.

A *coordinating conjunction* (*and*) provides a clue to the meaning of **extraordinary**. The words *but, or,* and *nor* are other coordinating conjunctions.
Note that a clue to the meaning of **astonish** is provided by using the word in a *series* of words that have similar meanings.
An *example* provides the key to understanding **mammoth**.

A form of the verb *to be* (*was*) links an example of a quality to the word **characteristic**.

Some of the dinosaurs were fierce, meat-eating creatures. Often, other *milder and gentler dinosaurs were unable to defend themselves from the more savage ones and thus became their* **victims**. Even the vegetarian dinosaurs who roamed about peacefully snacking on plants could be quite frightening to other species that shared the planet. A 55-ton brachiosaurus lumbering across the countryside would have presented a real **threat,** *a clear danger,* to any unsuspecting creature who got in its way. The huge Triceratops had frightening horns on its nose and over both of its eyes. The sight of this 10-ton animal bounding along at 30 miles per hour certainly scared the newly emerging mammals that had to scurry out of its way. Nevertheless, it was also a threat to any other dinosaur that tried to attack it.

Although groups of dinosaurs might be in **competition** with each other, *cooperation within a group was also common.* Members of a species might travel in a herd, eat and nest together, share responsibility for the young, and present a united defense against enemies.

Scientists are still debating about why the dinosaurs disappeared. We do not know for sure. All we know is that **twilight** *arrived for these creatures at the same time all across the earth. Then, in a twinkling, it was night,* and the dinosaurs were gone.

In a *cause-and-effect* relationship, one thing causes another thing to happen. The meaning of **victims** is established through a cause-and-effect relationship. *Thus* is a cause-and-effect clue word.

An *appositive phrase* contains a noun or pronoun that explains the noun or pronoun beside it. An appositive phrase indicates the meaning of **threat**.

Note that the meaning of **competition** is established through *contrast,* the placement of opposites near each other to point out their difference. The word *although* indicates contrast.

The meaning of **twilight** is established through *figurative language.* Figurative language is language that imaginatively describes one thing by comparing it to something else.

A Final Note

How can you learn strategic reading? Practice is a great way to improve your skill. The following lessons will help you learn the different context clues a writer uses. As you complete each lesson, you will become a more effective reader.

READING NEW WORDS IN CONTEXT

Lesson 1 CONTEXT: Amazing Nature

Introduction. What do you and your friends think about such creatures as Bigfoot and the Loch Ness monster? Are they just products of people's imagination, or do they really exist?

In the following article, a student writes for the school newspaper about some of the most famous mysterious creatures. The article gives you an opportunity to expand your vocabulary. Below are twenty Vocabulary Words that are used in the passage and in the exercise that follows it.

astonish	descendant	journalism	quote	symbol
conference	doubtful	legend	reliable	twilight
definite	innumerable	majority	session	unexpectedly
deny	interview	navigator	summarize	vivid

In Search of Bigfoot

The **conference** (1) here Saturday on the world's little-known, mysterious creatures was fascinating. This meeting made it clear to me that many people truly believe that some of these creatures exist but that others remain **doubtful** (2). Some of the information may **astonish** (3) you; it certainly amazed me!

Take Bigfoot, the large, ape-like creature reportedly seen throughout the United States for years. Is Bigfoot a **legend** (4), a myth, or a fanciful story? Is Bigfoot a real creature? Bigfoot, who walks on two feet, has been sighted by more than two thousand people. A man from California said that in 1967 a female Bigfoot **unexpectedly** (5) appeared in a clearing and then just as suddenly disappeared into the forest. The man took pictures of the creature. Experts have said the film could not have been faked. Thus many people trust the pictures as **reliable** (6) evidence. Some people think Bigfoot is a **descendant** (7) of or related across many generations to a prehistoric ape.

The Creature of Loch Ness

Because I study **journalism** (8), I collect and write about the news. What I heard during the conference about Scotland's Loch Ness monster certainly was news to me! I was able to **interview** (9) some interesting people about "Nessie." For example, I had a face-to-face discussion with a man from Scotland who claims he has seen the Loch Ness monster six times. He gave me a **vivid** (10) description of the monster: a dark creature, forty feet long, with one hump, a long neck, and a small head. He saw the creature rising out of the water shortly after sunset, during a foggy **twilight** (11). I wish I could **quote** (12) him, but he was so interesting that I forgot to write down his exact words. He thinks there are many of these creatures, perhaps giant mammals or reptiles, in Loch Ness. Scientists have tried to find the creatures with sonar, but they have found nothing certain, or **definite** (13), so far.

There also was a group meeting on sea monsters. During this **session** (14), a man who was a **navigator** (15) of a ship in the Bahamas said he once almost steered right into some sort of giant sea creature. He then told stories about the Lusca, a creature said to be part dragon and part octopus.

Not all scientists reject, or **deny** (16), the existence of the giant octopus.

Dinosaurs Live?

More than half of the people at the conference, a **majority** (17), attended my favorite **session**. It was about dinosaurs that still are seen in the tropics of central Africa. These dinosaurs are similar to sauropods, plant-eaters with long necks and small heads. The people in the Congo call the creatures Mokele-Mbembe. There have been **innumerable** (18) sightings, more than anyone can count. In 1983, a zoologist claimed to have seen one. Some scientists say it is not out of the question that dinosaurs still live there because the land was not covered with ice during the Ice Age.

To end, I will **summarize** (19) the main reason that many scientists think creatures like Bigfoot and the Mokele-Mbembe may exist. In brief, they point out that previously unknown animals continue to be discovered. For example, the Komodo dragon was discovered in 1912 and a new species of shark was discovered in 1976. The International Society of Cryptozoology (the study of mysterious animals) has a fitting **symbol** (20). The society is represented by a relative of the giraffe discovered by scientists in the late 1800s.

EXERCISE *Reading Strategically* ✍️

Directions. Answer each of the following items by circling the letter of the correct answer. You may need to refer to the selection as you answer the items. The numbers of the items are the same as the numbers of the boldface vocabulary words in the selection.

1. To give a clue to the meaning of **conference,** the writer
   (A) says that it was held here
   (B) refers to it in the next sentence as a meeting
   (C) says it was about little-known, mysterious creatures
   (D) refers to it as fascinating

2. You can tell from the article that people who are **doubtful** are
   (A) convinced
   (B) at the conference
   (C) unknown
   (D) not sure

3. In the article, **astonish** means to
   (A) amaze
   (B) inform
   (C) report
   (D) interest

4. All of the following are good definitions of **legend** *except*
   (A) a myth
   (B) a fanciful tale
   (C) a popular story passed down through the ages
   (D) a story based heavily on factual events

5. To let us know that when something happens **unexpectedly,** it happens without warning, the writer
   (A) says the event took place in a clearing in 1967
   (B) tells us that Bigfoot appeared and disappeared
   (C) connects **unexpectedly** with the word *suddenly*
   (D) hints that Bigfoot is real

6. The writer writes "many people trust the pictures as **reliable** evidence." Here, **reliable** means
(A) fake
(B) trustworthy
(C) on film
(D) not dependable

7. The writer explains that Bigfoot may be a **descendant** of a prehistoric ape. Here, **descendant** means
(A) something that has fallen from a great height
(B) someone or something related across generations
(C) something that rises to great heights
(D) someone or something related to a prehistoric ape

8. In the article, we learn that the writer's field is **journalism**. Here, **journalism** means
(A) writing books
(B) collecting and writing news
(C) attending conferences and panels
(D) reading about ideas

9. Which of the following is an example of an **interview** described by the writer of the article?
A) There was a group meeting that included the navigator's story about Lusca.
(B) The author learned about the Loch Ness monster.
(C) The author met interesting people.
(D) The author had a face-to-face discussion with a man from Scotland.

10. Which of the following is an example of a **vivid** description?
(A) I was able to interview some interesting people about "Nessie."
(B) I had a face-to-face discussion with a man from Scotland who claims he has seen the Loch Ness monster.
(C) The dark creature was forty feet long, with one hump, a long neck, and a small head.
(D) The man's accent made it difficult for me to write down his exact words.

11. The author writes, "He saw the creature rising out of the water shortly after sunset, during a foggy **twilight**." Here, **twilight** means
(A) after sunset but before dark
(B) early in the morning
(C) at noon
(D) when it is foggy

12. Which of the following is the reason that the writer is not able to **quote** the man from Scotland?
(A) The writer could not understand the Scotsman because of his heavy Scottish accent.
(B) The writer preferred to make up the information.
(C) The Scotsman had absolutely nothing new or interesting to say about the Loch Ness monster.
(D) The man was so interesting that the writer forgot to write down the exact words.

13. The writer says that scientists have not yet been able to discover anything **definite** about the Loch Ness monster. Here, **definite** means
(A) sonar
(B) certain
(C) so far
(D) giant

14. The writer's favorite **session** was about dinosaur sightings in Central Africa. Here, **session** means
(A) a group
(B) a heated debate
(C) a group meeting
(D) a sea monster

15. The writer of this article gives a clue to the meaning of **navigator**. What is the clue?
(A) The **navigator** steered the ship.
(B) The **navigator** saw a giant sea creature.
(C) The **navigator** captured the Lusca.
(D) The **navigator** told stories.

16. The writer tells us that not all scientists **deny** the existence of a giant octopus named the Lusca. Here, **deny** means to
(A) like
(B) publicize
(C) reject
(D) create

17. The author writes, "More than half of the people at the conference, a **majority**, attended my favorite **session**." Here, **majority** means
(A) a lot
(B) a few
(C) more than half
(D) a group of oddballs

18. The writer states that there have been **innumerable** sightings of the creature called Mokele-Mbembe. Here, **innumerable** means
(A) too few to count
(B) too many to be counted
(C) any number over one hundred
(D) sightings by zoologists

19. The writer concludes by saying, "To end, I will **summarize**." Here, **summarize** means
(A) to maintain
(B) to discover suddenly
(C) to continue
(D) to state briefly

20. You can tell from the article that a **symbol** is
(A) something that represents something else
(B) a relative of the giraffe
(C) a stunning scientific discovery
(D) something that is fitting

READING NEW WORDS IN CONTEXT

Lesson 2 | CONTEXT: Amazing Nature

Introduction. Tornadoes are the most violent of the world's winds. A tornado can have wind speeds of more than three hundred miles per hour. Many people also regard tornadoes as the most amazing or curious of the world's natural forces. What is it about tornadoes that causes amazement?

The following article gives you an opportunity to expand your vocabulary. Below are twenty Vocabulary Words that are used in the article and in the exercise that follows it.

aviation	demonstration	disturb	incident	nuisance
collapse	departure	exception	instinct	predict
collide	detect	fatal	locally	rash
complex	disastrous	foundation	miraculous	unfavorable

Beyond Oz: The Truth About Tornadoes

Dorothy and Toto landed in Oz before the days of **aviation** (1). They did not need to fly in an airplane. They had a natural form of travel—a tornado.

If you saw the movie *The Wizard of Oz,* you may recall the **miraculous** (2) landing of the girl and her dog. The miracle of their fall to earth is described in a work of fiction. However, real-life tornadoes also produce wonderful tales that sound amazing.

Truth Stranger Than Fiction

Many fascinating stories are told of tornadoes picking up animals or objects and carrying them away. During one true **incident** (3) in 1966 in Kansas, a tornado picked up a homemade cake and deposited it, completely undamaged, in a field in Missouri. Another occurrence involves the strange **departure** (4) of two women and a boy from a Missouri town in 1899. They went away quite suddenly when a tornado swept them up and carried them, unharmed, a quarter of a mile. One of the women later told about being in

the tornado. She said she did not crash into anything. She had been worried, though, that she would **collide** (5) with a wild horse that was also in the tornado.

In her book *These Happy Golden Years,* which is about prairie life in the late 1800s, Laura Ingalls Wilder includes a story about a tornado. The story provides a good **demonstration** (6) of a tornado's unusual abilities. It shows us how powerful a tornado can be as Laura describes one carrying away a small house. Later, after the storm has passed, the door of the house, undamaged, falls to the ground exactly where the house had been.

According to another tale, a tornado carried a house right off the **foundation** (7), the base on which it was built. The tornado had removed all the contents of the house except for two items. These **exceptions** (8) were a table and the gold-fish bowl on top of it. They remained quite unbothered. Who can say why the tornado did not **disturb** (9) the table and the goldfish bowl?

Raining Frogs and Fish

Some of these accounts make tornadoes seem as if they are playing tricks. Tornadoes, for example, have been known to pull the water right out of a river and then drop the water, sometimes including frogs and fish, on unsuspecting people. These assaults from the sky can be more than an annoyance, an inconvenience, or a **nuisance** (10). They can cause injury, too.

Many reliable people believe that stories such as these are true. However, many other people make it clearly known that they think some of these stories are nonsense. Their better judgment, or **instinct** (11), tells them that these things could not possibly happen in real life. You may want to ask some people within your community whether tornadoes have done unusual things **locally** (12).

It is important to remember that tornadoes can be **disastrous** (13). We should pay attention to the possible dangers from tornadoes. Tornadoes can cause much damage to property, and their force can cause one building, or an entire **complex** (14), to **collapse** (15)—just completely fall apart. They also can be **fatal** (16) to people. Most deaths from tornadoes result from flying debris.

At times, a **rash** (17) of tornadoes seems to occur around the country. It is not clear why many tornadoes break out suddenly. Experts use scientific instruments to locate **unfavorable** (18), or threatening, weather and to discover tornado formations. As a result, they now often can **detect** (19), or pinpoint, when tornadoes will occur. However, no one can tell beforehand exactly what will happen during a tornado. As you can imagine, it would be impossible to **predict** (20) the strange things tornadoes do.

EXERCISE *Reading Strategically*

Directions. Answer each of the following items by circling the letter of the correct answer. You may need to refer to the selection as you answer the items. The numbers of the items are the same as the numbers of the boldface vocabulary words in the selection.

1. The writer of this article about tornadoes gives a clue to the meaning of **aviation**. What is the clue?
   (A) The writer tells about Dorothy and Toto.
   (B) The writer mentions a natural form of travel.
   (C) The writer says the girl and her dog landed in Oz.
   (D) The writer relates the word to flying in an airplane.

2. The writer calls the landing of the girl and the dog **miraculous**. Here, **miraculous** means
   (A) related to stories
   (B) related to tornadoes
   (C) recalling
   (D) related to miracles

3. The writer refers to a true **incident**. Here, **incident** means
   (A) occurrence
   (B) tornado
   (C) homemade cake
   (D) deposit

4. Which of the following is an example of a **departure** that occurs in the article?
   (A) A homemade cake was dropped undamaged in a field.
   (B) Two women and a boy were swept away by a tornado.
   (C) Two women and a boy lived in Missouri in 1899.
   (D) Tornadoes can lift up very heavy items.

5. The writer says that although the woman did not crash into anything in the tornado, she did worry that she would **collide** with a wild horse. Here, **collide** means
   (A) to disagree
   (B) to harness
   (C) to crash
   (D) to sweep

6. According to the article, why is Laura Ingalls Wilder's story of the tornado a good **demonstration** of a tornado's abilities?
   (A) It happened in the late 1800s.
   (B) It is a true story about her youth.
   (C) It shows how powerful a tornado can be.
   (D) It is printed in a book that has been read by millions.

7. The writer says that a tornado carried a house off of its **foundation**. Here, **foundation** means
   (A) on the roof
   (B) the base on which the house was built
   (C) the size of the house
   (D) all the contents of the house

8. The article says that a tornado re-moved all the contents of a house with the **exceptions** of a table and a goldfish bowl. You can tell from the article that
   (A) the table and the goldfish bowl were the last things to disappear
   (B) the table, and the goldfish bowl were the first things to disappear
   (C) only the table and the goldfish bowl were untouched
   (D) the tornado was not very powerful

9. The writer asks, "Who can say why the tornado did not **disturb** the table and the goldfish bowl?" Here, **disturb** means to
   (A) bother
   (B) please
   (C) make
   (D) display

10. To give a clue to the meaning of **nuisance,** the writer
    (A) contrasts **nuisance** with the word *injury*
    (B) links **nuisance** to the words *annoyance* and *inconvenience*
    (C) says that a **nuisance** is an assault
    (D) links **nuisance** to the word *sky*

11. To give a clue to the meaning of **instinct,** the writer
    (A) links **instinct** to the words *believe* and *known*
    (B) links **instinct** to the word *nonsense*
    (C) links **instinct** to the phrase "their better judgment"
    (D) contrasts **instinct** with the word *judgment*

12. In the article, the writer states that you may want to ask people about the unusual things that tornadoes have done **locally**. Here, **locally** means
    (A) within a community
    (B) in a foreign country
    (C) recently
    (D) worldwide

13. Which of these is a reason that tornadoes may be **disastrous**?
    (A) People should take them seriously.
    (B) They can be very damaging to people and property.
    (C) Tornadoes can do unusual things.
    (D) Tornado stories can be very interesting.

14. The writer tells us that tornadoes can damage a **complex**. Here, **complex** means
    (A) group of people
    (B) entire city
    (C) set of buildings
    (D) several streets

15. In the article, **collapse** most nearly means to
    (A) be stronger
    (B) sway
    (C) be built
    (D) fall apart

16. The author writes that tornadoes can be **fatal** to people. Here, **fatal** means
    (A) lively
    (B) deadly
    (C) exciting
    (D) depressing

17. The writer says that, at times, a **rash** of tornadoes seems to occur. Here **rash** means
    (A) disorderly group
    (B) lack of notice
    (C) sudden outbreak
    (D) prediction

18. All of these are good definitions for **unfavorable** *except*
    (A) unsatisfactory
    (B) pleasing
    (C) not helpful
    (D) not approving

19. The writer explains that now experts can **detect** when tornadoes will occur. Here, **detect** means to
    (A) occur
    (B) escape
    (C) imagine
    (D) pinpoint

20. How does the writer let you know that to **predict** an event is to say ahead of time what will happen?
    (A) The writer says that it is impossible to tell beforehand what a tornado will do.
    (B) They writer says that tornadoes always do strange things.
    (C) The writer says that scientific instruments can discover tornado information.
    (D) The writer says that no one can prevent a tornado.

182 LESSON 2

Lesson 3 — CONTEXT: Amazing Nature

Introduction. There are spiders everywhere. No matter what you think about spiders, they are difficult to avoid. Here are some typical questions about spiders: How long have spiders existed? How many different kinds of spiders are there? What are some spider myths? How does a spider use its web? Is a spider an insect?

The following essay answers these questions and gives you an opportunity to expand your vocabulary. Below are twenty Vocabulary Words that are used in the essay and in the exercise that follows it.

abdomen	congratulate	flexible	heroic	mobile
caution	dread	foe	hoist	paralysis
commotion	error	generation	involve	previous
competition	escort	gratitude	maximum	separation

The Wide and Wonderful World of Spiders

Whenever they see a spider, some of my friends make a big **commotion** (1), rushing around and yelling. "Ooh, a spider!" they shout. "Get it away." Sure, they should be watchful and use **caution** (2) when near a few kinds of spiders, such as black widows. Most spiders, however, are harmless to humans. People should learn to overcome their fear of spiders and appreciate how helpful they really are.

For one thing, we should **congratulate** (3), or praise, the spider for its ability to survive. Did you know that spiders have been around for at least 300 million years? Fossils of spiders that old have been found.

There are at least 30,000 different kinds of spiders in the world. Some scientists think the **maximum** (4) may be more than 100,000 kinds. Of course, even that greatest possible number of spiders is a long way from the more than 700,000 different species of known insects!

Spiders versus Insects

You are mistaken if you think spiders are insects. Many people make such an **error** (5), though. How do you tell them apart? One way is to look at the **separation** (6) of each animal's body parts. A spider's body is divided into two sections: a head and thorax combination and an **abdomen** (7). The **abdomen** is the belly. An insect's body, on the other hand, has three parts. Also, a spider has eight legs, and an insect has six. And while an insect has feelers and often has wings, a spider does not.

Because most people give thanks to anything that gets rid of pests, we owe spiders some **gratitude** (8). They eat insects that are dangerous to plants and animals. Spiders are much more friend than **foe** (9) to humans.

Spiders vary greatly in size. People who are afraid of tiny house or garden spiders would **dread** (10) seeing a South American tarantula, which eats small birds. When walking in South America, people who are afraid of spiders probably would want an **escort** (11), someone to go with them.

The lowly spider may not seem like a brave or noble creature, but it has been a **heroic** (12) figure in many cultures for thousands of years. In an Achomawi Indian myth, for example, two brave spider brothers created the rainbow. A spider called Ananse is the hero of many African tales. For many years, parents have told these stories to their children. In this way, the stories have been handed down from one **generation** (13) to the next.

Spiders of Legend

Most myths about spiders **involve** (14) their ability to spin webs. One famous example comes from a Greek legend. According to this legend, a young girl named Arachne, who was a marvelous spinner and weaver, challenged the goddess Athena to a weaving **competition** (15). As a result of the contest, Athena became jealous and turned Arachne into a spider. Today, spiders are members of the class of animals called arachnids.

A spider's silk threads are strong but **flexible** (16). The thread bends without breaking to suit the spider's needs. A spider spins a lifeline thread as it moves from one place to another and as a result is easily **mobile** (17) in the air. The spider can **hoist** (18), or lift, itself by using its lifeline. Many spiders spin sticky webs in which to catch insects. The spider injects its victim with poison that causes a quick **paralysis** (19). The victim, which can no longer function on its own, is trapped. Did you know that a spider can make a brand new web or use a **previous** (20) one that it has swallowed? Like humans, spiders know the value of recycling!

EXERCISE *Reading Strategically*

Directions. Answer each of the following items by circling the letter of the correct answer. You may need to refer to the selection as you answer the items. The numbers of the items are the same as the numbers of the boldface vocabulary words in the selection.

1. To let us know that **commotion** may mean "noisy confusion," the writer
   (A) describes **commotion** as a peaceful time
   (B) describes **commotion** as "rushing around and yelling"
   (C) describes **commotion** as being friendly
   (D) describes **commotion** as a time of observation

2. You can tell from the essay that to use **caution** means
   (A) to be afraid
   (B) to be excited
   (C) to be watchful
   (D) to be foolish

3. What is the best meaning of **congratulate** as used in the second paragraph in this essay?
   (A) It means to praise.
   (B) It means to find.
   (C) It means to survive.
   (D) It means to be able.

4. In the article, **maximum** means
   (A) the greatest possible number
   (B) the least possible number
   (C) less than enough
   (D) more than enough

5. The writer says that people who think spiders are insects are in **error**. Here, **error** means
   (A) a correction
   (B) a difference
   (C) a decision
   (D) a mistake

6. Which of the following is an example of the **separation** of body parts of a spider?
   (A) A spider does not have feelers or wings.
   (B) A spider's body is divided into two sections.
   (C) An insect's body has three parts.
   (D) A spider has eight legs while an insect has six.

7. Another good word for **abdomen** is
   (A) head and thorax
   (B) feelers
   (C) belly
   (D) legs

8. Why does the writer believe that we owe spiders **gratitude**?
   (A) There are up to 100,000 types of spiders.
   (B) Spiders eat insects that can harm plants and animals.
   (C) Spiders should not be confused with insects.
   (D) We must be careful around some kinds of spiders.

9. The author writes, "Spiders are much more friend than **foe** to humans." Here, **foe** means
   (A) a fake
   (B) a mystery
   (C) a friend
   (D) an enemy

10. All of these are good definitions of **dread** *except* to
    (A) look forward to with fright
    (B) fear something in the future
    (C) be sad about something
    (D) be afraid of

11. The writer uses **escort** when talking about walking in South America. Here, **escort** means
    (A) a tarantula or other poisonous spider
    (B) a person who walks very quickly
    (C) a person who goes with another person
    (D) a person who is afraid of spiders

12. The writer says that the spider has been a **heroic** figure in many cultures for thousands of years. Here, **heroic** means
    (A) lowly
    (B) brave and noble
    (C) cultured and worldly
    (D) spiderlike

13. Passing tales from one **generation** to the next is most like
    (A) a sister giving a birthday present to a brother
    (B) parents handing down a quilt to their children
    (C) a child giving a grandparent a picture
    (D) a brother baby-sitting his little sister

14. The writer notes that most myths about spiders **involve** spiders' ability to spin webs. Here, **involve** means to
    (A) include
    (B) turn
    (C) disagree
    (D) reveal

15. In the article, the writer mentions a **competition** between the Greek goddess Athena and the weaver Arachne. Here, **competition** means

(A) a result
(B) a legend
(C) a contest
(D) a weaver

16. The best meaning of **flexible** as it is used in the article is the phrase

(A) made from silk
(B) bends without breaking
(C) strange and marvelous
(D) rigid and unbending

17. Why does the writer say that a spider is **mobile** in the air?

(A) A spider's threads allow it to move from place to place.
(B) A spider's sticky web allows it to catch insects.
(C) A spider's thread bends without breaking.
(D) A spider injects its victim with poison.

18. In the article, another good word for **hoist** is

(A) use
(B) injure
(C) spin
(D) lift

19. To give a clue to the meaning of **paralysis,** the writer

(A) mentions poison
(B) uses the word *inject* in the same sentence with **paralysis**
(C) says the victim can no longer function
(D) says that poison causes quick **paralysis**

20. To let us know that **previous** may mean "happening earlier than something else," the writer

(A) contrasts a **previous** web with a new web
(B) contrasts a web that one spider makes with a web that another spider makes
(C) hints that the spider will not make a web in the future
(D) indicates that **previous** is related to recycling

READING NEW WORDS IN CONTEXT

Lesson 4 | CONTEXT: Amazing Nature

Introduction. Do you ever watch the *Nature* series on public television? If so, you know that there are thousands of kinds of animals with all kinds of abilities. The animals and their abilities are pretty amazing.

The following article tells about some amazing animal abilities. The article gives you an opportunity to expand your vocabulary. Below are twenty Vocabulary Words that are used in the article and in the exercise that follows it.

acquire	discourage	hibernate	linger	requirement
conceal	disguise	imitate	portion	terminal
dainty	earnest	impostor	reference	vacuum
discomfort	gasp	inhale	regulate	vault

The Wild, Wonderful World of Animals

The animal kingdom is quite a place! If you take an **earnest** (1), or sincere, look at it, you will gain respect for the remarkable abilities of animals. You can also **acquire** (2) knowledge of animals' abilities by studying the animals or reading books about them. A serious study of the behaviors and abilities of various animals should be a **requirement** (3) for all students. Let's look at a few animals and their abilities and see if you agree that we all need to know something about the animal kingdom.

Hummingbirds are delicate and pretty, but these **dainty** (4) birds are also amazing flyers. They can stay in one place in the air while beating their wings more than fifty times a second. The common swift, however, certainly does not **linger** (5). It can fly for two to three hours at a time. A chimney swift may fly more than 100,000 miles in a year.

Animals Undercover

Many animals **disguise** (6) themselves for protection. For example, chameleons are lizards that can actually change color from green to brown to blend in with their surroundings. Some butterflies can look like the leaves they rest on. To protect themselves from an attack by another animal, hedgehogs roll themselves into a ball shape. Armadillos also try to avoid attacks in the same way. Many animals, such as moths and grasshoppers, can **conceal** (7) themselves by hiding near objects that are the same color or shape they are.

Other animals can **imitate** (8) the animals for which they are hunting. Some spiders, for example, act and move like the ants they are tracking. You could think of this kind of spider as an **impostor** (9), someone who deceives others by pretending to be something he or she is not.

Some animals spend the winter in an inactive, sleeplike state. Animals such as bears **hibernate** (10) in their dens so they can survive the cold winter season. During hibernation, these animals are able to adjust or **regulate** (11) their body temperatures. Their body temperatures go down for the winter to reduce the animals' need for food. The dormouse is another animal that avoids the **discomfort** (12) of hunger by hibernating. With its "thermostat" turned down, the dormouse sleeps comfortably in its nest. Some hibernating animals, such as bats, spend only a **portion** (13) of the winter, rather than the whole winter, asleep.

Have you ever wondered how some fish, frogs, and toads survive when their water supplies dry up? They survive by digging under the mud. They **inhale** (14), or breathe in air, through an opening to the surface.

Four-footed Animals in Flight

You may **gasp** (15)—or catch your breath suddenly in surprise—when you learn how far some animals can jump. The gray kangaroo can jump forty-four feet in one bound. Some animals, such as deer and large cats, can jump over high obstacles, too. Would you believe that a mountain lion has been known to **vault** (16) a nine-foot fence? That height would **discourage** (17) most other animals, but large cats are always sure of their abilities.

Many studies of interesting animal abilities include **references** (18) to the anglerfish. It is no wonder that this fish is mentioned. It comes equipped with its own fishing lure. This lure begins at the fish's mouth. The end, or **terminal** (19), part of the lure is lighted. The anglerfish actually "fishes" for other fish. Attracted by the lure, small fish swim toward the anglerfish. When they arrive, the **vacuum** (20) of the anglerfish's empty mouth greets them like a bottomless canyon.

EXERCISE   *Reading Strategically* ✍

Directions. Answer each of the following items by circling the letter of the correct answer. You may need to refer to the selection as you answer the items. The numbers of the items are the same as the numbers of the boldface vocabulary words in the selection.

1. To give a clue to the meaning of **earnest,** the writer
   (A) says animals have remarkable abilities
   (B) links **earnest** to the word *sincere*
   (C) says **earnest** is something you gain
   (D) implies that **earnest** is something you get by looking

2. The author writes that "you can also **acquire** knowledge of animals' abilities." Here, **acquire** means
   (A) need
   (B) lose
   (C) understand
   (D) gain

3. In the article, **requirement** means
   (A) important study
   (B) bad behavior
   (C) something needed
   (D) natural ability

4. You can tell from the second paragraph of the article that **dainty** means
   (A) delicate and pretty
   (B) large and clumsy
   (C) short and sweet
   (D) square

5. Which of the following is an example of how a bird can **linger**?
(A) The hummingbird stays in one place in the air by beating its wings rapidly.
(B) The hummingbird is a delicate and pretty animal.
(C) The common swift can fly for two to three hours at a time.
(D) A chimney swift can fly over 100,000 miles per year.

6. In the passage which of the following is an example of a way in which an animal can **disguise** itself?
(A) A butterfly can imitate an ant
(B) Lizards live in trees.
(C) An armadillo can sometimes avoid attack.
(D) A hedgehog can roll up like a ball.

7. The writer describes insects that can **conceal** themselves. Here, **conceal** means
(A) lose
(B) sell
(C) hide
(D) display

8. To let you know that to **imitate** may mean "to copy the actions of," the writer
(A) says some animals hunt other animals
(B) uses the words *spiders* and *ants*
(C) explains tracking
(D) uses the words *act* and *move like*

9. The writer says that you can think of a spider that acts like its prey as an **impostor**. Here, **impostor** means
(A) someone who looks like a spider
(B) something real
(C) someone who asks for money
(D) someone who pretends to be someone else

10. The author writes, "Animals such as bears **hibernate** in their dens so they can survive the cold winter season." Here, **hibernate** means to
(A) be very active
(B) live in a sleeplike state
(C) migrate to a warmer climate
(D) pace back and forth

11. To give a clue to the meaning of **regulate,** the writer
(A) links **regulate** with the word *adjust*
(B) refers to regular activities
(C) asks the reader to recall
(D) links **regulate** to the winter season

12. The author writes, "The dormouse is another animal that avoids the **discomfort** of hunger by **hibernating**." Here, **discomfort** means
(A) too much comfort
(B) lack of comfort
(C) cold weather
(D) low body temperature

13. You can tell from the article that a **portion** of the winter is less than the whole winter because the author uses the phrases
(A) "With its 'thermostat' turned down"
(B) "**hibernating** animals, such as bats"
(C) "the dormouse sleeps comfortably in its nest"
(D) "rather than the whole winter"

14. In this article, **inhale** means to
(A) breathe under water
(B) breathe out
(C) breathe through an opening
(D) breathe in

15. Which of the following is the most likely reason that you would **gasp** when you learned how far some animals can jump?

(A) You were bored.
(B) You did not understand.
(C) You were surprised.
(D) You were sad.

16. The author asks, "Would you believe that a mountain lion has been known to **vault** a nine-foot fence?" Here, **vault** means to

(A) jump over
(B) open a bank
(C) crawl under
(D) defeat an enemy

17. The writer says that a nine-foot fence would **discourage** most animals, but that a mountain lion is always sure of its ability. Here, **discourage** means

(A) to cause to be unsure about
(B) to make confident about one's abilities
(C) to display amazing courage and daring
(D) to make brave

18. To give a clue to the meaning of **reference,** the writer

(A) refers to the anglerfish
(B) uses the word *interesting*
(C) uses the word *mentioned*
(D) says the word is used in examinations

19. To let us know that **terminal** means "end," the writer

(A) says that the anglerfish "fishes" for other fish
(B) says most studies of animals' abilities mention the anglerfish
(C) says that the anglerfish's lure is lighted at the end part
(D) says that **terminal** is another word for *lighted*

20. How is the **vacuum** of the anglerfish's mouth most like a bottomless canyon?

(A) Both are places where animals live.
(B) Both are safe places to be.
(C) Both are full of water.
(D) Both are empty spaces.

READING NEW WORDS IN CONTEXT

Lesson 5 | CONTEXT: Amazing Nature

Introduction. Science kits or chemistry sets for young people have been popular for many years. Sometimes careers in science begin with these sets. Sometimes, too, young scientists startle and worry people with their experiments.

The following selection tells about a daring young scientist. The selection gives you an opportunity to expand your vocabulary. Below are twenty Vocabulary Words that are used in the selection and in the exercise that follows it.

bombard	gossip	particle	ransom	stray
bureau	jeopardy	pharmacy	receipt	surgery
conviction	license	pierce	resign	suspicion
flammable	lunar	pry	static	toll

The Adventures of Curious Jorge

Help! The natural world is in **jeopardy** (1) from my nephew, Jorge. He seems to be constantly involved with risky, and sometimes dangerous, projects. People are beginning to **gossip** (2) about him. I am afraid most of these rumors are true, too.

Jorge's first experiment was with **static** (3) electricity, electricity produced by rubbing one object against another. I am not sure what Jorge did, but he and his father had to **pry** (4) my sister Pepita's pancakes off the wall. It took a lot of force to remove the pancakes, too. After that, Jorge's father told him that he could not work with electricity without a **license** (5), or permit. Whether or not this is true, Jorge's electrical experiments have stopped for now.

Tides in the Bathtub
Lunar (6) cycles and tides caught his interest next. He thought that maybe the cycles of the moon affect the splashing of water in the bathtub as they affect the ocean tides. I just am not sure, but I have a **suspicion** (7) that Jorge is now

paying for a new bathroom carpet.

For a time, Jorge wanted to be a chemist. He mixed together chemicals in his science kit. He thought he had found cures for various illnesses. Jorge went to the drugstore to try to sell these chemical mixtures. At the **pharmacy** (8), Jorge began to **bombard** (9) the druggist with questions and ideas. Jorge seemed almost to be bombing him with his fast talk, and the druggist was so bothered that I thought he was going to **resign** (10)—just give up his position on the spot. Jorge even went to the local Medical Information Bureau. A **bureau** (11) is an agency that collects or gives information. Of course, Jorge's so-called medicines interested no one at the medical agency.

One day a wandering dog came to my sister's house. Noticing that the **stray** (12) dog was hurt, Jorge offered to perform an operation. "You can't perform **surgery** (13). You're just a young science experimenter. You're not a doctor," my sister told him.

Another time, Jorge wanted to find out how a fire extinguisher works. He poured vinegar and sodium bicarbonate together to form carbon dioxide. The mixture blew out a candle. Pepita made him do the experiment with the candle outside because there were too many **flammable** (14) items in the house. The linen curtains, for example, could easily be set on fire.

For a few weeks Jorge forgot about chemicals and became interested in machines. Designing little self-operating machines especially interested him.

"I'd like to design a city bus that is completely automatic," Jorge told me one day. In other words, no one would control it. There'd be no **toll** (15) for riding it, either—it would be free."

Jorge soon forgot about this idea, though, and went back to his science kit. Designing a bus must have been too big a project for him.

His next experiment, however, was not very popular. He tested the effects of light waves on earthworms. For some reason, he had to conduct the experiment in the kitchen. I think he needed a knife to **pierce** (16) holes in the shoeboxes in which he kept the worms. Making the holes was easy for him, but listening to Pepita wasn't.

"Don't leave any worms in here," my sister said, "and I don't want a **particle** (17) of dirt left, not even if it's as small as the head of a pin!"

I am partly to blame for Jorge's experiments. Last year, for his thirteenth birthday, I bought Jorge a science kit and two books of science experiments. I kept the written proof of my purchase, the **receipt** (18), from the store. Maybe I could return the kit and books. I guess it is too late for that, though. Anyway, all of Jorge's experimenting has led to something good. He's been accepted at a special school for gifted young scientists, so Jorge's **conviction** (19) of himself as a scientist has paid off. He always believed that he would succeed.

I just hope a mad scientist doesn't kidnap Jorge to get his secrets. We might not be able to find enough money to pay the **ransom** (20).

EXERCISE   *Reading Strategically* 👈

Directions. Answer each of the following items by circling the letter of the correct answer. You may need to refer to the selection as you answer the items. The numbers of the items are the same as the numbers of the boldface vocabulary words in the selection.

1. According to the essay, how does Jorge put the natural world in **jeopardy**?
(A) He sells his chemical mixtures.
(B) He is interested in animation.
(C) He enjoys designing self-operating machinery.
(D) He is interested in dangerous or risky projects.

2. To give a clue to the meaning of **gossip,** the writer
(A) relates it to the word *rumors*
(B) links it to risky projects
(C) links it to fear
(D) relates it to danger

3. **Static** electricity, according to scientific jargon, apparently means electricity
   (A) that flows through most ordinary power lines
   (B) that is used to power eggbeaters and most other small machines
   (C) that is created by cats
   (D) that is produced by rubbing one object against another object

4. In the selection, **pry** means to
   (A) force off with difficulty
   (B) snoop around
   (C) pray urgently and silently
   (D) paste with glue

5. What is the best meaning of **license** as used in the second paragraph of the article?
   (A) a safe place
   (B) a book
   (C) a permit
   (D) a careful driver

6. Which of the following is the reason that **lunar** cycles caught Jorge's interest?
   (A) He thought that the moon's cycles affected the movement of bath water.
   (B) He thought he could keep bath water from splashing out of the tub.
   (C) He found the mechanics of bikes and other cycles interesting.
   (D) He thought that lunar cycles made people act **suspiciously**.

7. You can tell from the article that to have a **suspicion** means to think something is true without being
   (A) worried
   (B) angry
   (C) sure
   (D) sincere

8. The writer says that Jorge went to the **pharmacy** to sell his chemical mixtures to the druggist. Here, **pharmacy** means
   (A) a supermarket
   (B) a drugstore
   (C) a clinic
   (D) a science kit

9. Jorge "began to **bombard** the druggist with questions and ideas." Here, **bombard** means to
   (A) attack
   (B) quiz
   (C) irritate
   (D) excite

10. The author writes, "The druggist was so bothered that I thought he was going to **resign**—just give up his position on the spot." Here, **resign** means to
    (A) enjoy work
    (B) become angry
    (C) make a sign
    (D) give up a position

11. The writer says that Jorge took his chemical mixtures to the Medical Information Bureau. Here, **bureau** means
    (A) the medical information in a science kit
    (B) a chest of drawers
    (C) a local drugstore
    (D) an agency that collects or gives information

12. Taking in a **stray** dog is most similar to
    (A) giving advice to a wandering musician
    (B) giving shelter to a homeless cat
    (C) going to see a traveling circus
    (D) operating on a person who is ill

13. Pepita told Jorge, "'You can't perform **surgery**. You're just a young science experimenter. You're not a doctor.'" Here, **surgery** means
   - (A) an operation
   - (B) a doctor
   - (C) a science project
   - (D) an experiment

14. Why didn't Pepita allow Jorge to do his experiment with the candles inside, near **flammable** items?
   - (A) Such items burn easily.
   - (B) Such items are everywhere.
   - (C) Such items are expensive.
   - (D) Such items are waterproof.

15. Jorge told the author that there would be no **toll** for riding his automatic bus. Here, **toll** means
   - (A) a door
   - (B) a payment
   - (C) a driver
   - (D) a bus

16. The author writes that Jorge "needed a knife to **pierce** holes in the shoeboxes in which he kept the worms." Here, **pierce** means
   - (A) to cut into many pieces
   - (B) to make a shoebox
   - (C) to make holes in
   - (D) to slice into strips

17. How could a **particle** of dirt left over from Jorge's experiment be like the head of a pin?
   - (A) Both are dirty.
   - (B) Both are very small.
   - (C) Both are sharp.
   - (D) Both were involved in Jorge's earthworm experiment.

18. Which of these is the most likely reason that the writer would save the **receipt** for the science kit?
   - (A) The science kit costs a lot of money.
   - (B) The **receipt** shows proof of purchase.
   - (C) The **receipt** tells how to cook something.
   - (D) The **receipt** gives instructions for the science kit.

19. All of the following are good definitions of **conviction** *except*
   - (A) a strong belief
   - (B) being convinced
   - (C) being proved guilty of an offense
   - (D) to act confused

20. In the article, **ransom** means
   - (A) the kidnapping of someone to keep them from conducting scientific experiments
   - (B) secrets stolen from a scientist
   - (C) money that is paid to someone who has been kidnapped
   - (D) money that is demanded for the return of someone who has been kidnapped

READING NEW WORDS IN CONTEXT

Lesson 6 CONTEXT: People and Places

Introduction. An anthropologist is a person who studies people and their cultures. People, of course, are part of the natural world, and their behavior is always interesting to examine. Margaret Mead (1901–1978) was a famous anthropologist. How did she become interested in this field, and what people did she study?

The following article answers these questions and gives you an opportunity to expand your vocabulary. Below are twenty Vocabulary Words that are used in the article and in the exercise that follows it.

analyze	destination	generous	profession	routine
biography	determination	identical	publicity	scholar
career	document	notion	reaction	self-confidence
debate	essential	offspring	respectable	thorough

The Life of an Anthropologist

Margaret Mead: The World Was Her Family is the title of one **biography** (1) of the anthropologist. The title of that book about Mead's life and **career** (2), or lifelong work, certainly is accurate. Mead's studies, writings, and ideas always got the public's attention because they received much **publicity** (3) through newspapers, magazines, and other popular media.

An Anthropologist Is Born

Mead was born in Philadelphia, the first child of Edward and Emily Mead. Both parents were involved in academics—he as an economics professor and she as a teacher and sociologist. They had four more **offspring** (4) in addition to Margaret. Mrs. Mead liked to **document** (5) her children's behavior, and the young Margaret also picked up the **routine** (6) of writing down her observations of her two young sisters. This regular procedure of observation and writing would be important in Margaret Mead's future.

At Barnard College in New York City, Mead was a good student. However, she was a **scholar** (7) without a clear direction until she took an anthropology course her senior year. Anthropology excited her because studying people was an **essential** (8) activity in her life. It was as basic and necessary to her life as eating and sleeping. How wonderful to think that doing what she loved could be her occupation, her **profession** (9)!

Travels in the Pacific

As a professional, Mead took her first field trip in 1925 to the Samoan islands in the Pacific Ocean. Because she felt sure of her abilities, Mead had **self-confidence** (10). Her goal was to make a complete, or **thorough** (11), study of the behavior of teenage girls there. Specifically, she investigated the **notion** (12) that teenagers are the same all over the world. Her conclusion after a year with the Samoan girls was that the idea that teenagers everywhere are **identical** (13) was false.

Her book *Coming of Age in Samoa* created **debate** (14) on the subject: Some critics supported her findings and others argued against them.

Mead's next **destination** (15) for field work was another place in the Pacific, Papua New Guinea. Here, she wanted to **analyze** (16) the native children's thoughts. The result of her detailed examination was her second book, *Growing Up in New Guinea*. This book also received ample, or **generous** (17), attention from the press and the public. Her response was a typical Mead **reaction** (18): She returned to the Pacific to study other cultures.

Mead's **determination** (19) to succeed in her own way guided her life, and this firm purpose took her far. Mead's accomplishments are highly **respectable** (20). For example, she was the author of thirty-nine books and many articles. She also made records and tapes. She was associated for years with the American Museum of Natural History and Columbia University, and she received many awards. In fact, by the time she died at the age of 77, Mead had headed so many organizations, made so many public lectures, and produced so many publications that she was a national celebrity.

EXERCISE · *Reading Strategically* ✍

Directions. Answer each of the following items by circling the letter of the correct answer. You may need to refer to the selection as you answer the items. The numbers of the items are the same as the numbers of the boldface vocabulary words in the selection.

1. To provide a clue to the meaning of **biography,** the writer
   (A) tells us that Margaret Mead was an anthropologist
   (B) tells us that the biography is about Mead's life
   (C) tells us that the title is accurate
   (D) tells us that the book is one biography

2. In the first paragraph of the article, **career** means
   (A) a vacation
   (B) a life
   (C) a lifelong work
   (D) a book

3. You can tell from the article that **publicity** is
   (A) information that makes something known to the public
   (B) studies, writings, and ideas about the lives of well-known biographers
   (C) money
   (D) scholarly writing read by only a few anthropology experts

4. You can tell from the article that **offspring** are
   (A) jobs
   (B) careers
   (C) ideas
   (D) children

5. To let us know that **document** may mean "to write down or record something," the writer

(A) says that Mrs. Mead was an observant parent
(B) says that Mrs. Mead disapproved of Margaret's observations
(C) notes that both Mrs. Mead and Margaret wrote down their observations
(D) considers writing a regular procedure

6. What does **routine** mean as it is used in the second paragraph of the article?

(A) writing
(B) observing
(C) a regular procedure
(D) having sisters

7. The writer explains that Mead was a scholar without a clear direction. Here, **scholar** means

(A) a person without direction
(B) a good student
(C) an area of anthropology
(D) a school

8. Which of the following is the most likely reason that the writer believes that studying people was an **essential** activity in Mead's life?

(A) It was basic and necessary to her life, just like eating and sleeping.
(B) It was an extravagant and wasteful use of her college education.
(C) Mead had no direction as a student.
(D) Mead was overjoyed to discover she could make a career of anthropology.

9. The author writes, "How wonderful to think that doing what she loved could be . . . her **profession**!" Here, **profession** means

(A) occupation
(B) obligation
(C) character
(D) direction

10. Which of the following is the most likely reason that the writer believes Margaret Mead had **self-confidence**?

(A) Mead was a scholar.
(B) Mead was an anthropologist.
(C) Mead felt sure of her abilities.
(D) Mead traveled around the world.

11. The writer says that in Samoa, Mead made a **thorough** study of the behavior of the islands' teenage girls. Here, **thorough** means

(A) considerate
(B) regular
(C) about other cultures
(D) complete

12. The author writes that Mead "investigated the **notion** that teenagers are the same all over the world." Here, **notion** means

(A) an idea
(B) a country
(C) an argument
(D) an agreement

13. The writer says that Mead concluded that teenagers are not **identical** all over the world. Here, **identical** means

(A) specific
(B) alike
(C) young
(D) worldly

14. Which of the following is the most likely reason that Margaret Mead's book about Samoan teenagers caused **debate**?

(A) Everyone agreed with her conclusions.

(B) No one thought she was correct.

(C) Everyone was critical.

(D) Some critics agreed with her and some disagreed.

15. Which of the following is an example of a **destination**?

(A) A **destination** is ample attention from the press.

(B) A **destination** is a detailed examination.

(C) A **destination** is Papua New Guinea.

(D) A **destination** is thoughts of native children.

16. Mead, says the writer, went to New Guinea "to **analyze** the native children's thoughts." Here, **analyze** means to

(A) study

(B) receive

(C) respond

(D) return

17. All of the following are good definitions of **generous** as used in this article *except*

(A) intelligent

(B) ample

(C) more than enough

(D) plenty

18. The writer states that Mead's response to the publication of her second book was "a typical Mead **reaction**." Here, **reaction** means

(A) the future

(B) the public

(C) a response

(D) a study

19. In the last paragraph of the article, **determination** means

(A) guidance

(B) Mead's life

(C) success

(D) firm purpose

20. Which of the following sentences is an example of one of Mead's **respectable** accomplishments?

(A) Mead's **determination** to succeed in her own way guided her life.

(B) This firm purpose took her far.

(C) Some critics supported her findings and others argued against them.

(D) She was the author of thirty-nine books and many articles.

READING NEW WORDS IN CONTEXT

Lesson 7 | CONTEXT: People and Places

Introduction. One of the greatest empires of the past belonged to the Aztecs in Mexico. The Aztecs were wandering warriors before settling in the area that is now Mexico City around A.D. 1200. They eventually dominated the region, but they first had to conquer the land. What natural difficulties did the Aztecs have to overcome? What was their capital city like? Who governed the empire? What were some of the Aztecs' beliefs?

The following selection gives you an opportunity to expand your vocabulary. Below are twenty Vocabulary Words that are used in the selection and in the exercise that follows it.

architect	consent	fragrant	management	sacrifice
betray	desperate	glimpse	plead	scheme
ceremony	district	ignite	quarantine	victim
conduct	eternal	interrupt	realm	victorious

Mexico's Aztec Heritage

If we could **glimpse** (1) Mexico's history during the 1400s, our quick look would find the Aztecs at the height of their power. The Aztec kingdom, or **realm** (2), was central Mexico. There they created a remarkable civilization.

The Floating Empire

Forming an empire in this area was not easy. The Aztecs began building their capital city, Tenochtitlan (tay-nawch-tee-TLAHN), on one of two islands in Lake Texcoco. The Aztecs soon expanded to the other island. To do so, they completed many canals, dams, and other engineering projects. The Aztecs did not have room to farm on the islands so they developed a clever **scheme** (3). This plan, which became highly successful, led to the creation of floating gardens in the lake.

The city's huge temple-pyramids and many buildings were just as impressive as the floating gardens. Clearly, the person responsible for designing the buildings, the **architect** (4), was extremely creative. Nearly two hundred thousand

people are thought to have lived in the city at one time. The city was divided into four major areas. One **district** (5) included the marketplace.

The Aztec empire was ruled by an emperor who had almost total power. The emperor had four chief advisers. He put a close relative in charge of the **management** (6) of internal affairs. With the control of internal affairs taken care of, the emperor was free to direct, or **conduct** (7), foreign matters. He lived in an enormous palace. Many gardens filled with sweet-smelling flowers surrounded the buildings in the palace area. As a result, the palace area was **fragrant** (8).

Aztec Religious Practices

For the Aztecs, military might and religion went together. The Aztecs usually were **victorious** (9) in battle. Because of their successes, they were known as Warriors of the Sun. To celebrate their victories, the Aztecs killed thousands of captives as a **sacrifice** (10) to their sun god and their god of war. Each **sacrifice** was offered to the gods in a ritual, or a **ceremony** (11). Some of the persons chosen to be killed and **sacrificed** considered the act an honor. Such persons would **consent** (12) to be sacrificed. Others who were chosen, however, considered themselves **victims** (13), helpless sufferers. Losing hope, these **desperate** (14) persons might **plead** (15) to be turned loose. However, their begging would fall on deaf ears because the priests would not **betray** (16) the gods. To turn against the gods would bring grief to the whole community.

The Aztecs used two calendar cycles. One calendar was a solar calendar that contained 365 days. The other was a 260-day religious calendar. The beginnings of these two cycles overlapped once every fifty-two years. The Aztecs believed that this period of overlap was a bad time. Normally, there would always be fires burning somewhere in the Aztec community. However, during this period, which was called Binding Up of the Years, the Aztecs thought it was necessary to **interrupt** (17) all fires. When the danger was past, priests started the fires burning again. They would **ignite** (18) all the fires in the temples. The Aztecs also believed they should protect pregnant women during this time. As a result, they would **quarantine** (19) pregnant women just as today we put some diseased persons in a separate place.

Since most powerful nations tend to think they will last forever, the Aztecs, too, probably thought their empire was **eternal** (20). However, it eventually fell to neighboring peoples and Spanish explorers of the 1500s.

EXERCISE *Reading Strategically* ✍

Directions. Answer each of the following items by circling the letter of the correct answer. You may need to refer to the selection as you answer the items. The numbers of the items are the same as the numbers of the boldface vocabulary words in the selection.

1. The author writes, "If we could **glimpse** Mexico's history during the 1400s, our quick look would find the Aztecs at the height of their power." Here, **glimpse** means to
   (A) read quickly
   (B) look quickly
   (C) find again
   (D) gain time

2. The writer explains that the Aztec **realm** was central Mexico. Here, **realm** means
   (A) a kingdom
   (B) a reality
   (C) quick glance
   (D) a civilization

3. The writer says that the Aztecs developed a clever **scheme** to make up for the lack of farm land on the islands. Here, **scheme** means
   (A) a room
   (B) an empire
   (C) a school
   (D) a plan

4. To give a clue to the meaning of **architect,** the writer
   (A) says that the **architect** lives in a city
   (B) links **architect** to the emperor's advisors
   (C) says that the **architect** must have been creative
   (D) says that an **architect** designs buildings

5. The writer claims that one **district** of the Aztec city included the market-place. Here, **district** means
   (A) an area
   (B) a shopping center
   (C) a city
   (D) a design

6. The **management** of internal affairs as described in the selection is most similar to
   (A) the direction of family matters
   (B) the fighting of a war
   (C) the construction of a temple-pyramid
   (D) the harvest of crops

7. To let us know that **conduct** may mean "to lead or direct," the writer
   (A) mentions an orchestra
   (B) gives **conduct** as another word for *direct*
   (C) links **conduct** to foreign matters
   (D) uses the word *enormous*

8. Which of the following is the most likely reason that the palace area was **fragrant**?
   (A) The palace was surrounded with sweet-smelling flowers.
   (B) A creative **architect** designed the palace and grounds.
   (C) The Aztec religion required the emperor's palace to be **fragrant**.
   (D) Both internal and foreign affairs were discussed in the palace grounds.

9. You can tell from the article that when the Aztecs were **victorious** in battle they
   (A) refused to fight
   (B) won
   (C) declared a tie
   (D) lost

10. To give a clue to the meaning of **sacrifice**, the writer
    (A) says that military might and religion went hand in hand
    (B) says that captives were always willing to be sacrificed
    (C) says a **sacrifice** is military victory
    (D) says that each **sacrifice** was offered to a god

11. The author writes, "Each **sacrifice** was offered to the gods in a ritual, or a **ceremony**." Here, **ceremony** means
    (A) a wedding
    (B) a serious matter
    (C) a ritual
    (D) a celebration

12. Which of the following is the most likely reason that a captive would **consent** to being offered to the gods?
    (A) The captive felt that it was an un-fair practice.
    (B) The captive believed that to be offered to the gods was an honor.
    (C) The captive was captured by the Aztecs in battle.
    (D) The captive begged to be set free rather than be offered to the gods.

13. The writer says that some of the cap-tives who were chosen to be offered to the gods considered themselves **victims**. Here, **victim** means
    (A) one who suffers
    (B) one who is willing
    (C) a hopeless person
    (D) an honorable person

14. The writer says that **desperate** prisoners begged to be set free. Here, **desperate** means
    (A) different
    (B) without hope
    (C) lonesome
    (D) diseased

15. The word **plead** in this article means to
    (A) refuse
    (B) hope
    (C) beg
    (D) ignore

16. Which of the following is the most likely reason that the priests would not **betray** the gods?
    (A) The priests would not pray to the gods on behalf of the captives.
    (B) The priests were deaf and could not hear the gods.
    (C) The priests believed that it was wrong to make offerings to the gods.
    (D) The priests believed that to turn against the gods would bring suffering upon the community.

17. All of the following are good definitions of **interrupt** *except* to
    (A) damage
    (B) cause a break in
    (C) stop
    (D) discontinue

18. The author writes that after the period called Binding Up of the Years had ended, the Aztec priests would **ignite** all the fires in the temples. Here, **ignite** means to
    (A) start a fire burning
    (B) be in a temple
    (C) extinguish
    (D) cover

19. How were pregnant Aztec women under **quarantine** during the Binding Up of the Years and people with certain sicknesses treated similarly?
    (A) They were both highly honored by Aztec priests.
    (B) They were both thought to be the disastrous results of the Binding Up of the Years.
    (C) They were both placed apart from the rest of the community.
    (D) They were both forbidden to put out fires during the Binding Up of the Years.

20. In the article, another definition for **eternal** is
    (A) doomed
    (B) unlikely to succeed
    (C) lasting forever
    (D) temporary

READING NEW WORDS IN CONTEXT

Lesson 8 | CONTEXT: People and Places

Introduction. The dominant mountain range on the North American continent is the Rocky Mountains. Many people just call them The Rockies. Map makers may tell you that the Rocky Mountains are officially part of the western mountain system known as the North American Cordillera. Where exactly are the Rocky Mountains? Where are the highest peaks in the range? How old is the range? Who were some early explorers?

The following article answers these questions and gives you an opportunity to expand your vocabulary. Below are twenty Vocabulary Words that are used in the article and in the exercise that follows it.

abundant	dramatic	flourish	marvel	satisfy
barrier	establish	inaccurate	numerous	survey
descriptive	extraordinary	irregular	possess	terrain
desirable	feat	leisure	prehistoric	vicinity

The Backbone of North America

Think of the Rocky Mountains as the continent's backbone. This comparison is **descriptive** (1) because it creates a picture of a lengthy, solid spine. In fact, the chain stretches for about 3,000 miles from New Mexico, north through the continental United States and Canada, and into northern Alaska. The peaks of the Rocky Mountains form the Continental Divide, which separates the continent's river systems. The Rockies have an **irregular** (2) width. For example, the range in Utah and Colorado is as wide as 300 miles across, but the mountains are less than 100 miles wide at the Canadian border.

The Rockies in the United States
The Rocky Mountains in the United States may be divided into four groups. The Southern Rockies range from New Mexico to central Wyoming. Colorado contains the highest and most striking, or **dramatic** (3), peaks in the Rocky Mountains, with 46 peaks over 14,000 feet high.

Mount Elbert (14,433 ft.) near Aspen, Colorado, is the highest peak in the Rockies. The Middle Rockies run from northwestern Colorado and northern Utah to the upper Yellowstone River in Montana, and they include the Teton range. The Northern Rockies begin in southern Idaho and continue to the Canadian border. They contain many glaciers, including the **numerous** (4) ones in the **vicinity** (5) of Glacier National Park in Montana. This area even has glaciers that can be reached easily on foot. Finally, the Brooks Range lies across northern Alaska. This range begins where the Canadian Rockies leave off.

For a mountain range, the Rocky Mountains are not old, although they were formed many years before recorded history. They date from the end of the Mesozoic era, about 60 to 70 million years ago. During that **prehistoric** (6) time, a large upheaval of the earth's crust created the Rocky Mountains.

Early Inhabitants and Explorers

Many American Indian peoples have lived in the Rocky Mountains, including the Navajo, the Shoshone, and the Ute. Europeans first started exploring the Rocky Mountains during the sixteenth century. That is when Francisco Vásquez de Coronado (1510–1554) of Spain led an expedition in the Southern Rockies. Explorers Meriwether Lewis (1774–1809) and William Clark (1770–1838) traveled the Northern Rockies in 1805 and 1806. Beaver trappers came to the Rockies in the 1820s. In 1830, some of these trappers joined together to **establish** (7) the Rocky Mountain Fur Company. Setting up this company was an important step in opening the Rockies to settlement. Noted explorer John Charles Frémont (1813–1890) also explored the Rocky Mountains. In Wyoming in 1842, Frémont succeeded in the **feat** (8) of climbing a 13,745-foot peak. As a result of his accomplishment, the mountain was named Frémont Peak. Frémont held the ranks of lieutenant, major, and finally general in the army. One of his duties was to inspect carefully the lands he explored. Because of Frémont's **survey** (9), the first scientific maps of the West could be created. Before this, any maps of the area would have been inaccurate (10) and often misleading.

As you can imagine, the Rockies at first created a **barrier** (11), like a wall of rock, for explorers and settlers going to the Pacific Coast from the east. Over time, however, explorers created trails that cut through the often rugged **terrain** (12), or ground. Some of these trails became highway and railroad routes.

The Rocky Mountains are a valuable source of precious metals. The Rockies have yielded much gold, silver, copper, and other minerals that are in high demand. Thus, the mountains have been a **desirable** (13) destination to fortune seekers.

The Rockies have been equally attractive to tourists. The mountains **satisfy** (14) tourists by answering their needs for mountain climbing, skiing, hiking, and other **leisure** (15) activities. Many people come to the Rockies simply to **marvel** (16) at the scenery. Their amazement is understandable because the Rockies **possess** (17) some of the most **extraordinary** (18), memorable, and spectacular scenery in North America. They also have plenty of wilderness areas—public parks in the Rockies are **abundant** (19). Beautiful trees and a variety of animals can be seen there, seeming to thrive and **flourish** (20) in this region.

EXERCISE *Reading Strategically* 👉

Directions. Answer each of the following items by circling the letter of the correct answer. You may need to refer to the selection as you answer the items. The numbers of the items are the same as the numbers of the boldface vocabulary words in the selection.

1. In the article, **descriptive** refers to something that
   (A) paints a picture
   (B) is lengthy and solid
   (C) is in the Rocky Mountains
   (D) is a backbone

2. Which of the following is an example of the **irregular** width of the Rocky Mountains?
   (A) The Rocky Mountains are three hundred miles wide at points in Utah and Colorado.
   (B) The Rockies are higher in some places than in others.
   (C) The peaks of the Rocky Mountains form the Continental Divide.
   (D) The Rockies are wider in some places than in others.

3. The writer says that Colorado contains the most **dramatic** peaks in the Rocky Mountains. Here, **dramatic** means

(A) mountainous
(B) striking
(C) populated
(D) coldest

4. What is the best meaning of **numerous** as used in the second paragraph of the article?

(A) few
(B) icy
(C) many
(D) some

5. The writer of this article gives a clue to the meaning of **vicinity**. What is the clue?

(A) The writer relates **vicinity** to Glacier National Park.
(B) The writer uses the preposition *of*.
(C) The word *area* follows **vicinity**.
(D) Information about glaciers follows **vicinity**.

6. You can tell from the article that **prehistoric** means

(A) before recorded history
(B) old-fashioned
(C) something about mountain ranges
(D) something more than 70 million years old

7. How does the writer let you know that to **establish** a business means to set up a business?

(A) The writer defines **establish**.
(B) The writer says that the Rocky Mountain Fur Company was set up in 1830.
(C) The words **establish** and *setting up* all refer to the beginning of the Rocky Mountain Fur Company.
(D) Both **establish** and *set up* sound businesslike.

8. All of the following are good definitions for **feat** *except*

(A) outstanding accomplishment
(B) everyday activity
(C) daring act
(D) admirable deed

9. John Charles Frémont was assigned to make a **survey** of unexplored lands in order to prepare a map. Making a **survey** of unmapped lands is most similar to

(A) washing a car before it rains
(B) looking at a map when lost
(C) farming in a harsh environment
(D) researching a report

10. You can tell from the article that **inaccurate** means

(A) scientific
(B) not exact
(C) of little help
(D) hidden

11. The writer says that the Rocky Mountains created a **barrier** for explorers and settlers headed to the Pacific Coast. To make this point more strongly, the writer says the **barrier** was like

(A) the Rocky Mountains
(B) the Pacific Ocean
(C) rugged ground
(D) a wall of rock

12. The writer says that explorers cut trails through the rugged **terrain** of the Rockies. Here, **terrain** means

(A) ground
(B) railroad line
(C) highway
(D) mountain

13. The author writes that the Rockies "always have seemed **desirable** to fortune seekers." Here, **desirable** means

(A) lucky
(B) attractive
(C) frightening
(D) metallic

14. The author writes, "The mountains **satisfy** tourists by answering their needs for mountain climbing, skiing, hiking, and other **leisure** activities." Here, **satisfy** means to
    (A) mountain climb
    (B) attract
    (C) answer needs
    (D) offer leisure activities

15. Which of the following is an example of a **leisure** activity that is mentioned in the article?
    (A) satisfaction
    (B) surveying
    (C) skiing
    (D) fortune hunting

16. To provide a clue to the meaning of **marvel,** the writer
    (A) lists **marvel** as a leisure activity
    (B) links the words **marvel** and *simply*
    (C) says that it is understandable that people **marvel**
    (D) links the words **marvel** and *amazement*

17. What is the best meaning of **possess** as it is used in the article?
    (A) attract
    (B) have
    (C) answer
    (D) need

18. All of the following are good definitions of **extraordinary** *except*
    (A) out of the ordinary
    (B) spectacular and unusual
    (C) exceptional
    (D) natural

19. The writer calls the public parks **abundant**. Here, **abundant** means
    (A) spectacular
    (B) memorable
    (C) plentiful
    (D) little

20. All of the following are good definitions for **flourish** *except*
    (A) dry up
    (B) succeed
    (C) grow
    (D) do well

READING NEW WORDS IN CONTEXT

Lesson 9 CONTEXT: People and Places

Introduction. Sparkling and colorful gemstones are sure attention-getters. Rings, earrings, necklaces, bracelets, and crowns frequently glow with gems. People have worked gems such as diamonds and emeralds into jewelry for thousands of years. When looking at cut and polished gemstones, a person may find it hard to believe that they came out of chunks of rock within the earth.

In the following story, an old jeweler tells an unusual story about his introduction to gems and to his life's work. The story gives you an opportunity to expand your vocabulary. Below are twenty Vocabulary Words that are used in the story and in the exercise that follows it.

ambitious	exclaim	knapsack	portrait	solitary
arid	heir	luxurious	reign	transparent
counterfeit	honorable	oath	relate	wardrobe
envy	investment	ornamental	request	yacht

The Prince's Jewels

Believe it or not, you are the first to **request** (1) that I **relate** (2) the story of how I became an expert on gems, nature's most beautiful and prized minerals. Since you have asked politely, I will be happy to tell you the story.

Strangely enough, my interest began years ago aboard a pleasure boat, a **yacht** (3), in the Mediterranean Sea. The boat was **luxurious** (4). Of course, anyone would expect it to be fancy and comfortable because it belonged to a prince. He was an **heir** (5) to a great fortune upon the death of his father, the king.

I was hired as a cabin boy on the **yacht** and was not much younger than the prince. At the time, I had just been through an **arid** (6), or unproductive, period in my life. Therefore, all I owned was either on me or in my **knapsack** (7), a kind of backpack. However, I was an **ambitious** (8) youth. When the prince realized I was eager to better myself, he offered to help me.

Opportunity Knocks

One day the prince, sunning himself alone aboard the **yacht,** started talking out loud about his latest **investment** (9), a rare diamond that he had bought in hopes of selling later for more money. As I listened to the prince, I became jealous. Fortunately, the prince was not aware of my **envy** (10).

The prince held up the diamond. "Why, I can see right through it. It is absolutely **transparent** (11)," the prince said. "This is the real thing. It's not **counterfeit** (12)," he continued.

Then to my complete surprise, I heard myself **exclaim** (13), like a child who cries out upon opening a marvelous present, "Sir, it's the most beautiful stone in the heavens!"

The prince, who had paid little attention to me before, just looked at me thoughtfully for several minutes. It seemed like hours to me.

"Yes," he said, as if answering himself. "I can see that you admire gems as much as I do. Would you like to learn about them with me?"

"Oh, yes," I replied.

"Very well," the prince said, "but you must take an **oath** (14) promising that you will never use the knowledge of gems for the purpose of creating false jewels. You and I will study diamonds, emeralds, rubies, sapphires, opals, turquoise, agate, jade, topaz, and other gems."

"With pleasure, sir," I replied.

A Student of Gems

From that day on, he taught me about gems. He showed me his valuable collection as well as pictures of famous gems.

"The **solitary** (15) stone in this necklace is a pink sapphire," he said. "It looks so splendid alone that it doesn't need any other stones with it. Remember that the sapphire is a type of mineral called *corundum*."

He pointed to a picture of the British Imperial State Crown with its famous black ruby. "This ruby would improve any clothes collection, not just the **wardrobe** (16) of the Queen of England."

"Such gems may be purely decorative, or **ornamental** (17), but the world can't have too much beauty," the prince added.

The prince showed me a **portrait** (18) of a beautiful woman. In the picture the woman was wearing the Hope Diamond, which is the largest blue diamond in the world.

Eventually the prince ruled the kingdom, and during this **reign** (19) I was his personal jeweler. When he died, I opened my own shop.

"I like gems," the prince once told me, "because they have such natural beauty and strength."

The prince was a good friend and an **honorable** (20) man. To show that I felt he was worthy of being greatly respected, I named my jewelry store The Prince's Gems.

EXERCISE *Reading Strategically* ☞

Directions. Answer each of the following items by circling the letter of the correct answer. You may need to refer to the selection as you answer the items. The numbers of the items are the same as the numbers of the boldface vocabulary words in the selection.

1. In this story, **request** means to
   (A) write formally
   (B) tell a story
   (C) ask politely
   (D) discuss briefly

2. In the story, the writer agrees to **relate** his tale. Here, **relate** means to
   (A) tell a story
   (B) ask for something
   (C) be happy
   (D) prize minerals

3. You can tell from the story that a **yacht** is
   (A) a board
   (B) a huge ocean liner
   (C) a canoe
   (D) a pleasure boat

4. All of these are good definitions of **luxurious** *except*
   (A) shabby and poor
   (B) fancy and comfortable
   (C) splendid and fine
   (D) rich and refined

5. According to the story, the prince is an **heir**. An **heir** is someone who
   (A) gives money away
   (B) works for a king
   (C) owns a yacht
   (D) inherits something

6. To give a clue to the meaning of **arid**, the writer
   (A) compares **arid** to age
   (B) links **arid** to the words *knapsack* and *backpack*
   (C) links **arid** to the word *unproductive*
   (D) contrasts **arid** with the word *ambitious*

7. The writer says that all he owned was either on him or in his **knapsack**. Here **knapsack** means a
   (A) yacht
   (B) cabin boy
   (C) backpack
   (D) shirt

8. To let you know that **ambitious** means "eager or desirous," the writer
   (A) was eager to clean cabins for the prince
   (B) remembers that he was poor
   (C) notes that he was younger than the prince
   (D) states that he was eager to better himself

9. According to the story, the rare diamond was an **investment** because the prince planned to
   (A) resell the diamond at a higher price
   (B) keep the diamond
   (C) give the diamond to the cabin boy
   (D) leave the diamond on the deck in the sun

10. Which of the following is an example of **envy** in the story?
    (A) The writer was eager to learn all that he could about gems.
    (B) The writer had a jealous reaction to hearing the prince's plan.
    (C) The prince offered to help the writer to better himself.
    (D) The prince intended to sell the gem.

11. In the story, the writer notes that the diamond is **transparent**. Here, **transparent** means
    (A) valuable
    (B) clear
    (C) absolute
    (D) real

12. To give a clue to the meaning of **counterfeit**, the writer
    (A) can see right through the diamond
    (B) says the prince called the gem "the real thing. . . . not **counterfeit**"
    (C) describes his complete surprise at the sight of such a beautiful gem
    (D) talks about the prince's money

13. When the writer heard himself **exclaim** in surprise, he was like
    (A) a child who cries out
    (B) a king being crowned
    (C) a person who becomes faint from shock
    (D) a beautiful stone

14. In the story, the prince says, "You must take an **oath** promising that you will never use the knowledge of gems for the purpose of creating false jewels." Here, to take an **oath** means to
    (A) devote your life
    (B) promise
    (C) study
    (D) learn about gems

15. You can tell from the story that
solitary means

(A) alone
(B) favorite
(C) splendid
(D) clustered

16. In the story, **wardrobe** means

(A) a crown
(B) a clothes collection
(C) a picture
(D) a gem collection

17. The writer uses **ornamental** when
talking about jewels. Here, **ornamental** means

(A) useful
(B) mechanical
(C) practical
(D) decorative

18. A **portrait** is the same thing as

(A) a beautiful woman wearing jewels
(B) a blue diamond
(C) a picture of someone
(D) a wealthy prince

19. The writer says, "The prince ruled the
kingdom, and during this **reign,** I was
his personal jeweler." Here, **reign**
means

(A) a kingdom
(B) the childhood of a prince
(C) the period of time a ruler is in
power
(D) a king's personal jewelry
collection

20. The writer calls the prince an
honorable man. Here, **honorable**
means

(A) beautiful, strong, and intelligent
(B) worthy of being respected
(C) like a gem
(D) certain

READING NEW WORDS IN CONTEXT

Lesson 10 | CONTEXT: People and Places

Introduction. Japan is a small country composed of four main islands and approximately four thousand smaller islands in the Pacific Ocean. However, it is one of the world's most important countries. It is highly industrialized and has a large population. What is the Japanese land like? What are Japan's natural resources?

The following article gives you an opportunity to expand your vocabulary. Below are twenty Vocabulary Words that are used in the article and in the exercise that follows it.

appropriate	contribute	exert	import	ordinarily
assume	cultivate	export	inviting	precipitation
boast	disadvantage	gorgeous	luscious	quantity
contrast	eliminate	hearty	occasion	tradition

The Pride of the Japanese

With good reason, the Japanese are proud of their land. One of the things they **boast** (1) of is the striking variety of Japan's geographical features. This variety is expressed in the **contrast** (2) between the snowcapped peak of Mount Fuji and the lowland plains. Mountains, agricultural fields, forests, and a rugged coastline **contribute** (3) to Japan's natural beauty. You could say that each adds to the wonder of the Japanese landscape. If you have seen pictures of the country's magnificent and delightful landscape, you have an idea of how **gorgeous** (4) and **luscious** (5) it is.

Do not **assume** (6) that the Japanese islands are flat just because they contain millions of people and several large cities. The truth is that more than three fourths of Japan is hilly and mountainous. After all, the islands were formed by volcanoes. There are 196 volcanoes in Japan, of which about thirty are active. **Ordinarily** (7), the volcanoes are not a problem, as significant eruptions are unusual. Japan's most famous peak, Mount Fuji,

looks threatening to some inexperienced hikers. However, it remains **inviting** (8) to mountain climbers who are enthusiastic, strong, and **hearty** (9).

Unique Farming Methods

The hills might be considered a **disadvantage** (10) for farmers. Instead, Japanese farmers have been able to make the land an asset rather than a drawback. Today's farmers still **cultivate** (11) the hillsides for growing crops in the same way that their ancestors prepared the land. They create terraces, or level surfaces, along the hillsides to hold the soil. The terraces also help hold water that runs down the hills. In the mountains, there is a great deal of rain and snow. This **precipitation** (12) enables rice, one of Japan's major crops, to grow. The annual rice festival is a big **occasion** (13) in rice-farming communities. This special event takes place in June or July.

Another of Japan's striking natural features is its forests. About half of Japan is covered with trees. Japan has a good timber industry. However, the Japanese are careful not to **eliminate** (14) all of their forests. To keep their forests from disappearing, they limit the cutting of trees.

Japanese Trade

Although it has many natural resources above ground, Japan does not have a large **quantity** (15) of mineral deposits below ground. For example, the amount of iron ore in Japan is small. As a result, Japan must rely on other countries and **import** (16) from them quite a few natural resources, such as iron ore. Many of these resources are necessary for Japan's huge **export** (17) trade.

Japan sells such products as motor vehicles, steel, and electronics to other countries.

In a discussion of Japan's natural treasures, it is suitable, or **appropriate** (18), to mention the country's coastline. The eastern shore is especially rugged and beautiful. In the picturesque coastal villages, people carry on a noble, vital **tradition** (19) of fishing the ocean around Japan. However, many of the people improve upon the custom of fishing by using modern techniques to catch the fish. In general, due to the effort that the Japanese put forth, or **exert** (20), to balance the time-honored with the new and improved, Japan is one of the world's success stories.

EXERCISE *Reading Strategically*

Directions. Answer each of the following items by circling the letter of the correct answer. You may need to refer to the selection as you answer the items. The numbers of the items are the same as the numbers of the boldface vocabulary words in the selection.

1. Which of the following is an example of something that the Japanese **boast** of?
   (A) They **boast** of the false notions outsiders have about Japan.
   (B) They **boast** of the large cities in Japan.
   (C) They **boast** of the lack of flat land to farm.
   (D) They **boast** of the striking variety of Japan's natural features.

2. To give a clue to the meaning of **contrast,** the writer
   (A) uses a high mountain and a low plain as an example of **contrast**
   (B) links **contrast** to the word *snowcapped*
   (C) says that anyone who has seen a picture of a Japanese landscape knows how gorgeous Japan is
   (D) says that the Japanese are proud of their land

3. In the article, **contribute** means to
   (A) take from
   (B) add to
   (C) say to
   (D) see clearly

4. By calling the landscape **gorgeous,** the writer is saying that the landscape is
   (A) flat
   (B) hilly
   (C) magnificent
   (D) rugged

5. In the article, another definition for **luscious** is
   (A) natural
   (B) pretty
   (C) pleasing the senses
   (D) mountainous and rocky

6. What is the best meaning of **assume** as used in the second paragraph of the article?
(A) It means to be surprised.
(B) It means to deny.
(C) It means to hope.
(D) It means to suppose.

7. How does the writer let us know that **ordinarily** means "usually"?
(A) The writer says that thirty of Japan's 196 volcanoes are active.
(B) The writer implies there is a problem with the number of volcanic eruptions in Japan.
(C) The writer predicts an eruption.
(D) The writer says that significant eruptions of Japan's active volcanoes are not usual.

8. All of the following are good definitions of **inviting** *except*
(A) threatening
(B) highly attractive
(C) tempting
(D) interesting

9. To give a clue to the meaning of **hearty,** the writer
(A) says Mt. Fuji can be threatening to some hikers
(B) says that Japan's mountains are a **disadvantage** to farmers
(C) links **hearty** to the words *enthusiastic* and *strong*
(D) relates **hearty** to the word *famous*

10. Japan's hills have not been a **disadvantage** to Japanese farmers because the farmers
(A) have put down their hoes and started a thriving tourist industry on the mountainsides
(B) have stopped farming the land the way that their ancestors did
(C) have realized that the mountains are a drawback and now farm only on the lowland plains
(D) have been able to keep the land from being a drawback through creative farming techniques

11. To **cultivate** land for growing crops as described in the article is most similar to
(A) hiking in the mountains
(B) harvesting a field of wheat
(C) putting the icing on a cake
(D) preparing a canvas for painting

12. The author says that **precipitation** allows rice to grow in the mountains. Here, **precipitation** means
(A) crops
(B) hills and mountains
(C) rain and snow
(D) dry land

13. The author writes, "The annual rice festival is a big **occasion** in rice-farming communities." Here, **occasion** means
   - (A) a special event
   - (B) a major crop
   - (C) people looking forward
   - (D) something solemn

14. How are the Japanese careful not to **eliminate** the trees of their forests?
   - (A) They do not allow a timber industry to exist.
   - (B) They keep the forests looking strikingly beautiful.
   - (C) They cut down more trees than they need.
   - (D) They do not overcut the trees.

15. The writer states, "Japan does not have a large **quantity** of mineral deposits below ground." Here, **quantity** means
   - (A) a mineral
   - (B) an amount
   - (C) a resource
   - (D) iron ore

16. The writer says that Japan relies on other countries and **imports** many natural resources. Here, **import** means
   - (A) to send to other countries
   - (B) to have no natural resources
   - (C) to bring in from other countries
   - (D) to buy only iron ore

17. You can tell from the article that to **export** something is to
   - (A) produce it
   - (B) bring it in from abroad
   - (C) send it abroad
   - (D) produce steel from iron ore

18. In the last paragraph of the article, **appropriate** means
   - (A) suitable
   - (B) lucky
   - (C) to be beautiful
   - (D) to take

19. The author writes that the Japanese "carry on a noble, vital **tradition** of fishing the ocean around Japan." Here, **tradition** means
   - (A) ocean fishing
   - (B) custom
   - (C) treasure hunt
   - (D) improvement

20. The writer discusses the effort the Japanese **exert** to balance the time-honored and the new. Here, **exert** means
   - (A) work
   - (B) maintain strongly
   - (C) put forth
   - (D) desire

READING NEW WORDS IN CONTEXT

Lesson 11 | CONTEXT: Ecology and Environment

Introduction. Where did you first hear about environmental issues? It may have been from your parents or a teacher, or from newspapers or television news reports. You also may have been exposed to environmental concerns from the picture books you read or had read to you as a child.

The following essay gives you an opportunity to expand your vocabulary. Below are twenty Vocabulary Words that are used in the essay and in the exercise that follows it.

appreciate	conscience	genuine	mammoth	theme
braille	doubtless	inform	plot	urge
campaign	entertain	inspiration	reduction	visual
characteristic	furious	juvenile	text	widespread

Environmental Literature for Kids

A sense of right and wrong about the environment may not begin at birth, but it can begin to grow shortly afterward. Such a sense is called a **conscience** (1). For many years, publishers of **juvenile** (2) literature have done their share to spread the save-the-environment message to their young readers. The best of these books **inform** (3), or tell, about specific problems and **entertain** (4) by amusing and interesting their readers.

Bill Peet, a former artist for the Disney Studios, wrote and illustrated *Farewell to Shady Glade* in 1966. The book has become an environmental classic for young readers. The story line, or **plot** (5) of the story, is built around various animals that are forced to leave their beloved Shady Glade because it is being destroyed by huge, **mammoth** (6), monster-like machines.

Another early environmental spokesperson for young readers was Theodor Seuss Geisel, also known as Dr. Seuss (1904–1991). In 1971, Dr. Seuss wrote *The Lorax*. In this book, an unusual creature called the Lorax begins a **campaign** (7) against environmental pollution. As part of its

plan, the Lorax says that the trees cannot speak for themselves, so he must speak for them. He stands on a tree stump and shouts angrily and loudly. He is **furious** (8) about the effects of pollution on the Truffula Trees, the Humming Fish, the Swomee Swans, and the Brown Bar-ba Loots. Young readers **appreciate** (9) the Lorax's colorful world, and they also value his message.

Twenty years later, author-illustrator Lynne Cherry also speaks for the trees in her book *The Great Kapok Tree*. Her written **text** (10) and the paintings that go with it focus on the preservation of the Amazon rain forest. Cherry went to the rain forest of Brazil to research her illustrations of plants, animals, and insects. The book features maps showing the original area covered by the world's rain forests and the much smaller area that the rain forests cover today. This **reduction** (11) of trees alarms environmentalists.

The Great Kapok Tree is a **visual** (12) treat. However, it is more than just pleasing to look at. Its message is timely and important. The book features various animals that **urge** (13) a man not to chop down a great kapok tree. Each of their attempts to convince the man tells the reader something about the relationships among the plants and animals of the rain forest.

One of today's foremost authors and illustrators of picture books, Chris Van Allsburg (b. 1941), also tackles the environmental problem. His book *Just a Dream* (1990), deals with environmental concerns in a mysterious manner **characteristic** (14), or typical, of Van Allsburg's style. In Van Allsburg's story, a young boy named Walter litters, does not believe in sorting trash to recycle, and makes fun of planting trees for future generations. One night, though, Walter has a dream about a future time when the earth is ruined by **widespread** (15) pollution. The thought of pollution covering a large area of the planet sincerely

concerns Walter. As a result, he wakes up with a **genuine** (16) feeling of responsibility toward the environment. The idea of taking responsibility for the environment is central to the book. It is a **theme** (17) that is timely and that deserves our attention.

It is **doubtless** (18) that these books and others about the environment have reached thousands of young readers. The number of these books that have been sold proves that their audience is large. The books certainly have been an **inspiration** (19) for many readers by influencing their lives and pushing them towards new ideas. In addition to regular English editions, some juvenile books also are available in other languages and in special editions such as **braille** (20), a system of writing for the visually impaired.

EXERCISE   *Reading Strategically* ✍

Directions. Answer each of the following items by circling the letter of the correct answer. You may need to refer to the selection as you answer the items. The numbers of the items are the same as the numbers of the boldface vocabulary words in the selection.

1. To provide a clue to the meaning of **conscience,** the writer
   (A) tells us that many books for young readers deal with the environment
   (B) tells us that a **conscience** is a sense of right and wrong
   (C) tells us that a **conscience** develops early in a child's life
   (D) tells us that a **conscience** is damaging to the environment

2. To let us know that **juvenile** may mean "suitable for young people," the writer
   (A) links **juvenile** to literature
   (B) links **juvenile** to birth
   (C) links **juvenile** literature to the words *young readers*
   (D) links **juvenile** to books about the environment

3. The writer explains that the best books **inform** their readers. Here, **inform** means to
   (A) amuse
   (B) entertain
   (C) tell
   (D) worry

4. You can tell from the article that **entertain** means to
   (A) **inform**
   (B) amuse and interest
   (C) have a conscience
   (D) publish

5. What is the best meaning of **plot** as used in the second paragraph of the article?
   (A) children's literature
   (B) building
   (C) large animal
   (D) story line

6. In the second paragraph of the article, **mammoth** means
   (A) huge
   (B) destructive
   (C) noisy
   (D) green

7. To provide a clue to the meaning of **campaign,** the writer
   (A) identifies it as personal
   (B) relates it to the environment
   (C) refers to it as a plan
   (D) is against it

8. The author writes that the Lorax "is **furious** about the effects of pollution on the Truffula Trees, the Humming Fish, the Swomee Swans, and the Brown Bar-ba Loots." Here, **furious** means
   (A) loud
   (B) standing on a tree stump
   (C) very angry
   (D) interested in pollution

9. The writer says that young readers **appreciate** the Lorax's message as well as his colorful world. Here, **appreciate** means
   (A) readers
   (B) message
   (C) dislike
   (D) value

10. The author writes, "Her written **text** and the paintings that go with it focus on the preservation of the Amazon rain forest." Here, **text** means
    (A) written part of book
    (B) preservation
    (C) illustrations and drawings
    (D) book cover

11. To let us know that **reduction** means "the amount by which something is made smaller," the writer
    (A) hints that the rain forests are near extinction
    (B) links the **reduction** of trees and land to the shrinking area of the rain forest
    (C) says that the **reduction** of trees is due to environmentalists
    (D) says that Lynne Cherry's book features maps

12. You can tell from the article that **visual** means
    (A) timely and important
    (B) foremost
    (C) connected with sight
    (D) having to do with

13. All of the following are good definitions of **urge** *except*
    (A) convince
    (B) persuade politely
    (C) ask earnestly
    (D) force

14. The writer uses **characteristic** to describe Chris Van Allsburg's mysterious manner of writing because
  (A) a mysterious manner is typical of his writing
  (B) everyone's manner is mysterious
  (C) no one understands his books because they are very mysterious
  (D) his manner is usually never mysterious

15. Walter, the hero of Chris Van Allsburg's *Just a Dream*, dreams of **widespread** pollution that poisons the planet. Here, **widespread** means
  (A) a map of a large area
  (B) covering a large area
  (C) separated from a large area
  (D) devastated

16. Which of the following is the most likely reason that Walter's feeling of responsibility toward the environment is **genuine**?
  (A) He didn't believe that **widespread** pollution was a real concern.
  (B) He woke from a troubled sleep.
  (C) His dream made him sincerely concerned about it.
  (D) He did not remember why his dream worried him.

17. The author says that taking responsibility for the environment is a **theme** of Van Allsburg's *Just a Dream*. Here, **theme** means
  (A) commitment
  (B) haunting vision
  (C) timely
  (D) main idea

18. According to the article, why is it **doubtless** that books about the environment have reached many readers?
  (A) Only foreign language editions have sold well.
  (B) Book sales prove that the books have a large audience.
  (C) Book sales show that not many people are interested in the books.
  (D) Many people are **doubtful** that books can help save the environment.

19. In the last paragraph of the article, **inspiration** means
  (A) a timely vision
  (B) a deep breath of air
  (C) a positive influence
  (D) books

20. The best meaning of **braille** as used in the article is
  (A) writing for the visually impaired
  (B) writing for young readers
  (C) writing for non-English-speaking people
  (D) writing for all students

READING NEW WORDS IN CONTEXT

Lesson 12 | CONTEXT: Ecology and Environment

Introduction. Sarah Cynthia Sylvia Stout, a character in a poem by Shel Silverstein, ran into problems because she would not take the garbage out. Today, the whole planet is running into problems because there is too much garbage to take out. How much garbage is there? What can be done?

The following article gives you an opportunity to expand your vocabulary. Below are twenty Vocabulary Words that are used in the selection and in the exercise that follows it.

adjust	corporation	foul	issue	remedy
applaud	disgust	guidance	merchandise	revolution
ballot	dissolve	hazard	persuade	temporary
candidate	employer	inexpensive	protest	villain

The Garbage Glut

Have you ever walked past a trash can on the street and noticed a **foul** (1), dirty, or rotten smell? The awful smell came from garbage.

Does the sight of litter and trash in the streets, along highways, and in public parks **disgust** (2) you? It sickens most people.

Garbage, Garbage, Everywhere

Do you worry about what eventually will happen to all the **merchandise** (3) in the stores? Much of the goods bought and sold in stores will end up as garbage.

We all produce garbage. It will not go away. Garbage lasts a long time; it is not a **temporary** (4) problem.

The **issue** (5) of garbage is part of a broader question that has to do with people's attitudes toward the environment. This question is finally being addressed. A **revolution** (6) is taking place in the way people think about garbage. Many people have completely changed their lifestyles in order to create less garbage. Many of these people have also tried to **persuade** (7) others to do the

same. Have you been talked into reducing your garbage output?

Some eye-opening statistics may help convince you. It is estimated that each person in the United States discards an average of about four pounds of garbage every day. Such activity is not criminal, but it makes every person a **villain** (8) in the fight against garbage. An average family may throw away more than two tons of garbage a year. Most of this trash goes to overcrowded landfills where much of it will not break up for many years. For example, nonrecyclable plastics will take almost forever to **dissolve** (9). Some of the garbage is toxic. There is a risk that a toxic material will get into the soil and water and create dangers for humans. Therefore, toxic garbage can become a **hazard** (10) to the environment and public health.

What You Can Do

What can you do? There are many ways you can help **remedy** (11) or relieve the garbage problem:

• First, change your own habits so that you produce less garbage. Recycle all that you can, including paper, cardboard, glass, cans, and aluminum. You can also recycle clothes, food, and many other items around your home. Get used to reusing what you can. If you **adjust** (12) in this way, your changes can make a big difference.

• Talk to people about the need to recycle and not throw away so much garbage. Most people want to help. They just need advice, or **guidance** (13).

• Urge people to support a **candidate** (14) running for public office who has a concern about the environment and will work for improved recycling programs. When a person votes, his or her **ballot** (15) should count for the environment.

• Ask each adult you know if his or her place of employment has a recycling program. If not, urge the adult to talk to his or her **employer** (16) about beginning one. If the boss is worried that such a program may cost too much, explain that the program can be **inexpensive** (17) and easily organized. Check with a local or state recycling program for details.

• If a local company is a big garbage producer, challenge that **corporation** (18) to recycle. The people that own and work for a company usually will listen to concerned citizens.

• Write letters of **protest** (19) if you object to a company's overuse of packaging or the packaging of products in nonrecyclable containers.

• Be sure to let individuals or companies that do a good job with garbage know that you **applaud** (20) and approve of their efforts.

EXERCISE *Reading Strategically*

Directions. Answer each of the following items by circling the letter of the correct answer. You may need to refer to the selection as you answer the items. The numbers of the items are the same as the numbers of the boldface vocabulary words in the selection.

1. The writer of the article wonders if you have ever walked past a trash can and noticed a **foul** smell. Here, **foul** means
(A) pleasant and cheery
(B) silly
(C) rotten or awful
(D) delicious

2. All of the following are good definitions of **disgust** *except* to
(A) cause a feeling of excitement
(B) sicken
(C) produce a feeling of distaste
(D) make ill or repulse

3. To give a clue to the meaning of **merchandise,** the writer
(A) links **merchandise** to goods bought and sold
(B) uses the synonym *garbage*
(C) disapproves of **merchandise**
(D) notes that people throw away **merchandise**

4. The writer reminds us that the garbage problem is not **temporary.** Here, **temporary** means
(A) lasts a long time
(B) does not last a long time
(C) gigantic
(D) will never go away

5. The writer explains that the **issue** of garbage is part of a broader question. Here, **issue** means
   - (A) garbage
   - (B) a publication
   - (C) an attitude
   - (D) a question

6. You can tell from the article that **revolution** means
   - (A) a complete change
   - (B) the environment
   - (C) many people
   - (D) time when no change takes place

7. To give a clue to the meaning of **persuade,** the writer
   - (A) hints that to **persuade** is to bring about revolution
   - (B) links **persuade** to our throwaway society
   - (C) connects **persuade** to creating less garbage
   - (D) asks if you have been talked into producing less garbage

8. The writer uses **villain** to describe people who throw away too much trash. Here, **villain** means
   - (A) hero
   - (B) fighter
   - (C) do-gooder
   - (D) wrongdoer

9. To let you know that **dissolve** means to break up or melt, the writer
   - (A) notes that trash in landfills takes a long time to break up
   - (B) hints that plastics are filling up landfills
   - (C) thinks that our system of recycling is breaking down
   - (D) explains that melting plastic is the best way to recycle it

10. Which of the following is an example of a way that toxic garbage can be a **hazard**?
    - (A) Toxic garbage is easy to store.
    - (B) People are learning to produce less toxic garbage.
    - (C) Toxic garbage can get into the water supply.
    - (D) Toxic garbage can be recycled.

11. You can tell from the article that **remedy** means to
    - (A) worsen
    - (B) relieve
    - (C) ignore
    - (D) emphasize

12. To let us know that **adjust** may mean "to change in order to correct," the writer
    - (A) lists several ways people can make a difference by changing their habits
    - (B) tells what can and cannot be recycled
    - (C) wants to make a difference
    - (D) says people should throw away everything now before the landfills are closed

13. In the article, another word for **guidance** is
    - (A) need
    - (B) hope
    - (C) advice
    - (D) people

14. In the article, a person who is a **candidate** is
    - (A) elected
    - (B) running for public office
    - (C) concerned about the environment
    - (D) not interested in what people say

15. The author writes, "When a person votes, his or her **ballot** should count for the environment." Here, **ballot** means

(A) opinion
(B) experience
(C) vote
(D) dislike

16. The writer uses **employer** when talking about the place one works. Here, **employer** means

(A) place
(B) recycler
(C) friend
(D) boss

17. In the article, a program that is **inexpensive**

(A) is too expensive
(B) is not easily organized
(C) is not possible
(D) does not cost a lot

18. You can tell from the article that **corporation** means

(A) a garbage producer
(B) the people that own and work for a company
(C) a group of concerned citizens who organize to make changes in a company's policies
(D) people who listen to citizens' comments

19. Which of the following is the most likely reason that you would write a letter of **protest** to a company?

(A) You agree with the company's policies and want to encourage it to continue on the same track.
(B) You want to know more about the company's policies.
(C) You object to the company's policies.
(D) You want to apply for a job with the company.

20. You can tell from the article that **applaud** means to

(A) approve
(B) dislike
(C) distrust
(D) envy

READING NEW WORDS IN CONTEXT

Lesson 13 | CONTEXT: Ecology and Environment

Introduction. You do not have to leave the city to appreciate and defend nature. Some people do, however. Some people move to the country or to the woods so they can experience more of nature firsthand. They also want to be where they can help protect nature from pollution and destruction.

The following selection tells about a remarkable woman who decided to move to the woods. The selection allows you an opportunity to expand your vocabulary. Below are twenty Vocabulary Words that are used in the selection and in the exercise that follows it.

absorb	debt	mourning	rebel	self-respect
amateur	duplicate	offense	regret	simplify
complaint	intrusion	omit	resident	sympathy
cooperate	keen	privacy	security	tension

Goodbye to the City

Anne LaBastille needed to get away. She wanted to escape the strain of city life and the **tension** (1) caused by the demands people made on her. She felt the need to **rebel** (2) against the control of the city. She also wanted to resist the control that other people had over her life. In other words, she wanted a less complicated way of living. To **simplify** (3) her life, she decided to go to the woods to live. This may seem like an extreme response, but it made sense for LaBastille, a wildlife ecologist. (An ecologist is a biologist who studies the relationship between living things and their environment.) She built a cabin by Black Bear Lake and another one by Lilypad Lake in the Adirondack Mountains of northern New York.

Walden Revisited

Her popular books, including *Woodswoman* and *Beyond Black Bear Lake,* reveal no troubled feeling, or **regret** (4), about her lifestyle. She clearly is in **sympathy** (5) with Henry David Thoreau, the American writer and naturalist who went to live alone with nature at Walden Pond in the 1800s. This shared understanding is clear to anyone who has read Thoreau's classic work, *Walden.*

LaBastille built her first log cabin at Black Bear Lake in the mid-1970s. She named the cabin *West of the Wind.* She enjoyed exploring the woods and lakes, day and night. She felt that she was a **resident** (6) not only of her cabin but also of the woods. She considered the woods her home. LaBastille also enjoyed serving as a guide to visitors. She especially liked helping women gain a sense of personal worth, of **self-respect** (7), through camping and backpacking experiences.

Because she lived and worked in nature, nature came to **absorb** (8) all of LaBastille's time. It took up her attention completely both in relaxing and in working. She soon began sharing her sharp, enthusiastic, and **keen** (9) insight into nature by writing books and articles for such magazines as *National Geographic.* Readers could tell that she was a professional, not an **amateur** (10), ecologist.

Trouble in Paradise

However, advancing civilization started interrupting LaBastille's peaceful life at Black Bear Lake. One type of **intrusion** (11) was the people who kept making demands on her personal life. As a result, it became increasingly difficult for LaBastille to keep her **privacy** (12). She found that **security** (13), even in the woods, became a concern. For example, she had to lock the cabin doors at night.

Another **intrusion** into LaBastille's peaceful life came from the sky. The ecologist became extremely concerned about acid rain in the Adirondacks. She voiced her **complaint** (14), or protest, through her writings. Because she knew that people everywhere must work together to prevent acid rain, she urged all nations to **cooperate** (15) to stop acid rain. She also considered the spraying of chemicals by airplanes an **offense** (16) against nature and joined with other Black Bear Lake **residents** to stop the harmful practice.

Perhaps to escape the creeping advance of civilization, LaBastille decided to build a cabin deeper in the woods in 1984. LaBastille recognized that she owed Thoreau thanks for his inspiration. So she paid her **debt** (17) by naming her new cabin, which was on Lilypad Lake, *Thoreau II*. However, the new cabin was not a copy or a **duplicate** (18) of Thoreau's cabin. LaBastille's cabin was smaller than Thoreau's. To his cabin, Thoreau had added a root cellar in which to store food. LaBastille, however, did not want a root cellar; she chose to **omit** (19) it from her design.

Unlike Thoreau, LaBastille did not live completely alone. She had the companionship of her devoted Pitzi, a German shepherd. German shepherds are great companions for women living alone in the woods, LaBastille writes. Pitzi lived with LaBastille during her first years at Black Bear Lake. LaBastille grieved when Pitzi died. However, following a period of **mourning** (20) for Pitzi, she got two other German shepherds, Condor and Chekika.

EXERCISE *Reading Strategically*

Directions. Answer each of the following items by circling the letter of the correct answer. You may need to refer to the selection as you answer the items. The numbers of the items are the same as the numbers of the boldface vocabulary words in the selection.

1. To give a clue to the meaning of **tension,** the writer
   (A) compares it to modern life
   (B) says it is caused by wildlife
   (C) links it to strain
   (D) says that ecology is the study of **tension** in modern life

2. The writer explains that Anne LaBastille felt the need to **rebel** against the control of the city. Here, **rebel** means
   (A) to agree
   (B) to resist
   (C) to control
   (D) to escape

3. Which of the following is a reason that Anne LaBastille wanted to **simplify** her life?
   (A) She had always wanted to live in the woods.
   (B) Her life had become too complicated.
   (C) She was a wildlife ecologist.
   (D) Her life was no longer difficult enough.

4. The best meaning of **regret** as used in the article is
   (A) a happy feeling
   (B) a change in lifestyle
   (C) a troubled feeling
   (D) looking forward hopefully

5. You can tell from the article that **sympathy** means
   (A) shared feeling or understanding
   (B) resentment toward naturalists
   (C) disagreement
   (D) partnership

6. Which of the following is a reason that LaBastille felt that she was a **resident** of the woods?
   (A) She was a hermit.
   (B) She owned the woods.
   (C) She never felt as safe in the woods as she did inside her cabin.
   (D) She felt that the woods were her home.

7. In the third paragraph of the article, **self-respect** means
   (A) selfishness
   (B) a sense of personal worth
   (C) a sense of loneliness
   (D) the ability to survive in the wilderness

8. Which of the following is an example of the way that nature came to **absorb** LaBastille's time?
   (A) LaBastille tried to get away from nature in her free time.
   (B) LaBastille could not relax even when she was not working.
   (C) It was clear that LaBastille was a professional ecologist.
   (D) Nature took up all of LaBastille's attention, both off work and on.

9. All of the following are good definitions of **keen** *except*
   (A) leisurely
   (B) enthusiastic
   (C) piercing
   (D) sharp

10. The author writes, "Readers could tell that she was a professional, not an **amateur,** ecologist." Here, **amateur** means
    (A) not professional
    (B) professional
    (C) young
    (D) old

11. Which of the following is an example of an **intrusion** that bothered LaBastille?
    (A) People made demands on her personal life.
    (B) LaBastille never had any visitors and became lonely.
    (C) LaBastille found that she could not control her temper around visitors.
    (D) The people of Black Bear Lake wished that LaBastille would keep to herself.

12. Which of the following is the most likely reason that LaBastille could not keep her **privacy**?
(A) She became lonely.
(B) She did not like living in the public eye.
(C) People frequently came to visit her.
(D) Someone stole it when she left her door unlocked.

13. How does the writer let you know that **security** may mean "protection" or "safety"?
(A) The writer compares the word to a secret.
(B) The writer says **security** was a concern.
(C) The writer talks about Thoreau.
(D) The writer points out the need to lock cabin doors.

14. The writer says that LaBastille voiced her **complaint** about acid rain through her writing. Here, **complaint** means
(A) praise
(B) concern
(C) protest
(D) commitment

15. You can tell from the article that **cooperate** means to
(A) protest
(B) work together
(C) complain
(D) fight

16. The author writes that LaBastille "considered the spraying of chemicals by airplanes an **offense** against nature." Here, **offense** means
(A) protective measure
(B) harmful action
(C) natural purpose
(D) agreement

17. The writer says that LaBastille paid her **debt** to Thoreau by naming her second cabin after him. Here, **debt** means
(A) a mortgage payment
(B) a copy of an original
(C) a rent payment
(D) something that is owed

18. Thoreau II, says the author, "was not a . . . **duplicate**, of Thoreau's cabin." Here, **duplicate** means
(A) a payment for a debt
(B) something that is larger
(C) a copy
(D) something that is smaller

19. Choosing to **omit** a root cellar from the design of a house is most similar to
(A) choosing to put a paragraph back in an essay
(B) choosing to leave a paragraph out of an essay
(C) choosing to rewrite a paragraph of an essay
(D) choosing to publish an essay in a school newspaper

20. The writer notes that after a period of **mourning**, LaBastille got two other dogs. Here, **mourning** means
(A) grieving
(B) peace
(C) before noon
(D) looking for

READING NEW WORDS IN CONTEXT

Lesson 14 | CONTEXT: Ecology and Environment

Introduction. The world's largest land animals—elephants—are in trouble. Both the African elephant and its slightly smaller relative the Indian elephant are on the endangered species list. Why are they in trouble? What is being done to help the elephants?

The following essay gives you an opportunity to expand your vocabulary. Below are twenty Vocabulary Words that are used in the essay and in the exercise that follows it.

benefit	migrate	provoke	severe	tragedy
captivity	obvious	reckless	suburbs	unfortunate
decrease	prey	resemble	survival	unite
eavesdrop	prohibit	responsibility	threat	vocal

Elephants in Danger

Elephants are big (an African elephant can stand thirteen feet tall), but a little tender, loving care still can **benefit** (1), or help, them. In fact, many people and governments have realized what a **tragedy** (2) it would be to lose all of the world's elephants. This disaster probably will not occur. New laws and plans are helping to keep elephants alive. As a result, the species' chances of **survival** (3) may be improving.

The Ivory Trade

Perhaps you have seen pictures of a killing of a herd of elephants. Irresponsible, uncaring, and **reckless** (4) people have wiped out whole elephant herds because they wanted ivory tusks to sell. The ivory trade was a major reason for the **decrease** (5) in the numbers of elephants in both Africa and Asia. For example, the estimated population of African elephants went from 1,300,000 in 1979 to 600,000 in 1989. The sudden decline would **provoke** (6), or cause, lawmakers to make changes. New laws have been passed that **prohibit** (7) the killing of elephants for their tusks. These laws

forbidding the wasteful killing are a positive development. It is **unfortunate** (8) however, that elephants still are hunted as **prey** (9) by illegal hunters. The unlucky elephant is still a victim of hunters who disobey the law.

A new and harsher **threat** (10) to the elephants is from increasing human populations in Africa and Asia. This possible danger is, in fact, the most **severe** (11) one facing elephants. People are taking more and more of the elephants' grazing lands for new developments. The elephants' homes are being destroyed to make room for **suburbs** (12), towns on the edges of cities. Some countries have recognized their **responsibility** (13), or obligation, to the elephants. These countries have made it their duty to create protected wildlife parks. Elephants, like humans, need enough land to maintain their societies and families. Elephants need plenty of land because they **migrate** (14), moving from place to place in search of food.

Zoos also help to save the elephants, but their role is small. Many animals do not act the same in confined areas as they do in the wild. The Indian elephant, for example, rarely reproduces in **captivity** (15). Even the most modern zoo is not an adequate substitute for the elephant's natural environment.

Speaking Out to Help the Elephant
Increased public awareness about the nature of elephants also is important. The more people know and care about the elephant, the more **vocal** (16) they should become. Speaking out is an important step in the efforts to save the elephants. We already know that elephants **resemble** (17) humans in some ways. They may be even more similar to us than we know. It is **obvious** (18) that elephants are intelligent and sensitive. It is also clear that they have a strong sense of family. They seem to feel many emotions. Some people have seen elephants cry. Just imagine what we might discover if we could listen in, or **eavesdrop** (19), on a conversation among elephants. Don't you think people should **unite** (20) and, by working together, save these creatures?

EXERCISE *Reading Strategically* ☞

Directions. Answer each of the following items by circling the letter of the correct answer. You may need to refer to the selection as you answer the items. The numbers of the items are the same as the numbers of the boldface vocabulary words in the selection.

1. You can tell from the article that if we **benefit** the elephants, we _____ them.
(A) like
(B) adjust
(C) help
(D) stand by

2. The author writes, "Many people and governments have realized what a **tragedy** it would be to lose all of the world's elephants." Here, **tragedy** means
(A) relief
(B) comedy
(C) plan
(D) disaster

3. To provide a clue to the meaning of **survival**, the writer
(A) speaks of having a plan
(B) refers to keeping the elephant species alive
(C) refers to having a disaster
(D) tells about governments making new laws

4. To give a clue to the meaning of **reckless**, the writer
(A) describes people and elephants
(B) uses **reckless** in a sentence with the words *wiped out*
(C) places **reckless** in a series with the words *irresponsible* and *uncaring*
(D) refers to whole herds

5. Which of the following is an example of a **decrease** that is mentioned in the article?
(A) The elephant population dropped between 1979 and 1989.
(B) The writer mentions two different years.
(C) The amount of elephants' grazing land taken for development has risen.
(D) The writer includes the detail of the number of tons of ivory sold.

6. In the article, **provoke** means
   (A) attack
   (B) cause
   (C) encourage
   (D) want

7. In the article, **prohibit** means to
   (A) be legal
   (B) forbid
   (C) allow at certain times
   (D) relate to elephants

8. All of these are good definitions of **unfortunate** *except*
   (A) unfavorable
   (B) not fortunate
   (C) unlucky
   (D) positive

9. The best meaning of **prey** as used in the article is
   (A) someone who hunts illegally
   (B) someone who hunts elephants
   (C) something that is hunted
   (D) to weigh heavily on someone

10. You can tell from the article that **threat** means
    (A) a possible danger
    (B) a population
    (C) an elephant
    (D) a fact

11. Another word that means nearly the same thing as **severe** is
    (A) kind
    (B) threatening
    (C) increasing
    (D) harsh

12. The writer explains that the elephants' land is being destroyed to make room for **suburbs.** Here, **suburbs** means
    (A) towns built outside of cities
    (B) underground
    (C) homes for elephants
    (D) built on elephants' grazing grounds

13. The writer uses **responsibility** when talking about some countries' obligations to elephants. Here, **responsibility** means
    (A) emotion
    (B) duty
    (C) recognition
    (D) laws

14. To give a clue to the meaning of **migrate,** the writer
    (A) describes in great detail the elephants' diet
    (B) notes how elephants move from place to place
    (C) explains that elephants need a lot of sleep
    (D) describes the life of elephants that live in zoos

15. In the article, **captivity** means
    (A) outside a zoo
    (B) inside a zoo
    (C) the natural environment of free, wild animals
    (D) behavior of zoo animals

16. The author writes, "The more people know and care about the elephant, the more **vocal** they should become." Here, **vocal** means
    (A) outspoken
    (B) worried
    (C) publicly aware
    (D) written

17. The writer uses **resemble** to explain how elephants are like humans. Here, **resemble** means to

(A) know
(B) have more
(C) be larger than
(D) be similar to

18. The best meaning of **obvious** as used in the article is

(A) difficult to see
(B) clear
(C) just like an elephant
(D) senseless

19. **Eavesdrop** in this article means to

(A) join in
(B) sit in
(C) listen in
(D) talk like elephants

20. Which of the following is an example of how people can **unite** to save the elephant?

(A) People can listen in on elephants' conversations.
(B) People can work hard to save the elephant.
(C) People can work together to save the creatures.
(D) People can be similar to the elephant.

READING NEW WORDS IN CONTEXT

Lesson 15 CONTEXT: Ecology and Environment

Introduction. You may have thought concerns about the environment and ecology started in this century. They did not, however. Many early voices of warning came during the nineteenth century. Some of these were from American Indians who loved the land.

The following letter gives you an opportunity to expand your vocabulary. Below are twenty Vocabulary Words that are used in the letter and in the exercise that follows it.

anthem	compliment	hesitate	pollute	reservoir
apologize	courteous	impatience	promotion	specify
application	engage	justify	qualify	superior
associate	frantic	nominate	rehearsal	toxic

Dear Cara,

I wish you could have been at my school's Earth Day celebration this year. Last year's event was good but ordinary. By contrast, this year's celebration was far **superior** (1). My teacher asked if she could **nominate** (2) me as chairperson of the celebration. Deep down, I was unsure whether I wanted to be named to the position. I did not **hesitate** (3) in giving my answer, though. I agreed to accept the position without delay.

Why? It occurred to me that we could use Earth Day to honor one of my heroes, Chief Seattle (1790–1866). Have you heard of him? He was a chief of the Suquamish and the Dwamish nations in the Pacific Northwest in the 1800s. We can still find many **applications** (4) today for Chief Seattle's words about the environment, which were made before most people had thought about the dangers of **toxic** (5), or poisonous, wastes that **pollute** (6) and damage the waters and air. As a result, my committee and I decided to put his words to use during the Earth Day celebration. People were encouraged to think about the environment when they heard Chief Seattle's words. Everyone

really responded well. Because it furthered our cause, I feel that the theme, Chief Seattle Talks About the Earth, was a successful **promotion** (7).

I think the following quotations will **justify** (8) my admiration of Chief Seattle. See if they aren't reason enough for you.

•"The air is precious. It shares its spirit with all the life it supports."

•"The earth is our mother. What befalls the earth befalls all the sons and daughters of the earth."

•"What is man without the beasts? . . . Whatever happens to the beasts also happens to the man."

Chief Seattle was a brave and noble leader. He also was **courteous** (9). The quotations above show his politeness and grace. He spoke these gentle words to United States officials who wanted to buy the land of his defeated people.

For Earth Day, some students wrote a sentimental song about Chief Seattle. Others used the chief's words to compose an **anthem** (10) to his ideas. This song of devotion to Chief Seattle was very moving.

Another group wrote and performed a short play about Chief Seattle. The play was not going well until the final practice. At that **rehearsal** (11) the play finally began to work. The actors represented a variety of animals, such as eagles, wolves, deer, bears, and horses. In the play, each of these animals was an **associate** (12) of Chief Seattle's at his meetings in Washington, D.C. They joined with him to tell about the earth. Using the animals was a clever idea of the writer, a friend of mine. I gave her a **compliment** (13) after the play, and I truly meant the praise.

As portrayed in the play, Chief Seattle showed no **impatience** (14) with government officials. He was calm and did not seem to mind the endless government delays and interruptions. As a result, no one ever viewed him as **frantic** (15). He had a large supply, a **reservoir** (16), of strength as he urged his

listeners to respect the land of his ancestors.

Chief Seattle did not define, or **specify** (17), exactly what people should do to protect the environment. However, he asked people to love and preserve the land, water, and air "for your children's children."

His ideas definitely would **qualify** (18) him as one of the country's first and greatest environmental spokespersons. Don't you think he would be fit for such a position? If he were alive today, Chief Seattle surely would **engage** (19), or join, in Earth Day celebrations.

Well, I'm sorry my letter is so long! Therefore, I do **apologize** (20). I thought you would be interested in Chief Seattle, though. I hope to hear from you soon.

Sincerely,

Kevin

EXERCISE *Reading Strategically*

Directions. Answer each of the following items by circling the letter of the correct answer. You may need to refer to the selection as you answer the items. The numbers of the items are the same as the numbers of the boldface vocabulary words in the selection.

1. To let us know that **superior** does not mean "ordinary," the writer
   - (A) contrasts **superior** with something ordinary
   - (B) says that **superior** means "good"
   - (C) compares an event to a celebration
   - (D) shows that **superior** means "worse than ordinary"

2. In the letter, **nominate** means to
   - (A) reject
   - (B) be chairperson
   - (C) be unsure of oneself
   - (D) name to a position

3. The writer says he did not **hesitate** in giving his answer. Therefore, he did not
   - (A) delay
   - (B) hurry
   - (C) agree to
   - (D) honor

4. The writer explains that even today we can find **applications** for Chief Seattle's words. Here, **applications** means
   - (A) worthy causes
   - (B) uses
   - (C) personal information
   - (D) a variety of things

5. To give a clue to the meaning of **toxic,** the writer
   (A) links **toxic** to the word *pollute*
   (B) links **toxic** to the word *poisonous*
   (C) suggests that **toxic** relates to the environment
   (D) contrasts **toxic** to the words *waters* and *air*

6. In the letter, **pollute** means all the following *except*
   (A) to do harm
   (B) make unclean
   (C) infect
   (D) disinfect

7. The writer says that the theme, "Chief Seattle Talks About the Earth" was a successful **promotion** because
   (A) it was spoken by Chief Seattle
   (B) it was a good cause
   (C) it furthered the cause
   (D) the writer found few uses for Chief Seattle's words

8. You can tell from the letter that **justify** means to
   (A) deny strongly
   (B) give reasons for
   (C) tell everyone
   (D) admire strongly

9. Another good word for **courteous** is
   (A) rude
   (B) polite
   (C) aloof
   (D) honorable

10. The writer mentions that some students "used the chief's words to compose an **anthem.**" Here, **anthem** means
    (A) regional music
    (B) a song sung only on Earth Day
    (C) a song of devotion
    (D) any song written by students

11. Another definition for **rehearsal** is
    (A) practice
    (B) refusal
    (C) public performance
    (D) try-out

12. The writer tells about a play in which different animals acted as **associates** to Chief Seattle. Here, **associate** means
    (A) agent
    (B) representation of an animal
    (C) fellow representative
    (D) politician

13. Which of these is the most likely reason that the writer gave his friend a **compliment**?
    (A) The writer disliked the play she wrote.
    (B) The writer thought he could write a better play.
    (C) The writer had ideas about making the play she wrote better.
    (D) The writer thought the play she wrote deserved praise.

14. Which of the following is an example of how Chief Seattle showed no **impatience**?
    (A) Chief Seattle was calm and polite.
    (B) Chief Seattle had a large supply of strength.
    (C) Chief Seattle praised the writer's clever idea.
    (D) Chief Seattle did not know what to do.

15. To give a clue to the meaning of **frantic,** the writer
    (A) connects **frantic** to a view
    (B) contrasts **frantic** and the word *calm*
    (C) says **frantic** describes result
    (D) uses **frantic** as a synonym of *calm*

16. In this letter, **reservoir** means
  (A) a reservation
  (B) reserved
  (C) a large supply
  (D) very little

17. The writer notes that Chief Seattle did not define or **specify** what people should do for the environment. Here, **specify** means to
  (A) be special
  (B) define
  (C) speculate
  (D) protect

18. The writer explains that Chief Seattle's ideas "certainly would **qualify** him as one of the country's first . . . environmental spokespersons." Here, **qualify** means to
  (A) make unsuited for a position
  (B) make too good for a position
  (C) make fit or suited for a position
  (D) improve the quality of something

19. In the last paragraph of the letter, **engage** means to
  (A) join in
  (B) agree to marry
  (C) be lively
  (D) disapprove of

20. The writer feels a need to **apologize** because he _____ writing such a long letter.
  (A) is happy about
  (B) is proud of
  (C) hopes he succeeded in
  (D) is sorry about

Vocabulary Words

abdomen
absorb
abundant
acquire
adjust
amateur
ambitious
analyze
anthem
apologize
applaud
application
appreciate
appropriate
architect
arid
associate
assume
astonish
aviation

ballot
barrier
benefit
betray
biography
boast
bombard
braille
bureau

campaign
candidate
captivity
career
caution
ceremony
characteristic
collapse
collide
commotion
competition
complaint

complex
compliment
conceal
conduct
conference
congratulate
conscience
consent
contrast
contribute
conviction
cooperate
corporation
counterfeit
courteous
cultivate

dainty
debate
debt
decrease
definite
demonstration
deny
departure
descendant
descriptive
desirable
desperate
destination
detect
determination
disadvantage
disastrous
discomfort
discourage
disguise
disgust
dissolve
district
disturb
document
doubtful

doubtless
dramatic
dread
duplicate

earnest
eavesdrop
eliminate
employer
engage
entertain
envy
error
escort
essential
establish
eternal
exception
exclaim
exert
export
extraordinary

fatal
feat
flammable
flexible
flourish
foe
foul
foundation
fragrant
frantic
furious

gasp
generation
generous
genuine
glimpse
gorgeous
gossip

gratitude
guidance

hazard
hearty
heir
heroic
hesitate
hibernate
hoist
honorable

identical
ignite
imitate
impatience
import
impostor
inaccurate
incident
inexpensive
inform
inhale
innumerable
inspiration
instinct
interrupt
interview
intrusion
investment
inviting
involve
irregular
issue

jeopardy
journalism
justify
juvenile

keen
knapsack

Vocabulary Words (continued)

legend
leisure
license
linger
locally
lunar
luscious
luxurious

majority
mammoth
management
marvel
maximum
merchandise
migrate
miraculous
mobile
mourning

navigator
nominate
notion
nuisance
numerous

oath
obvious
occasion
offense
offspring
omit
ordinary
ornamental

paralysis
particle
persuade

pharmacy
pierce
plead
plot
pollute
portion
possess
precipitation
predict
prehistoric
previous
prey
privacy
profession
prohibit
promotion
protest
portrait
provoke
pry
publicity

qualify
quantity
quarantine
quote

ransom
rash
reaction
realm
rebel
receipt
reckless
reduction
reference
regret
regulate

rehearsal
reign
relate
reliable
remedy
request
requirement
resemble
reservoir
resident
resign
respectable
responsibility
revolution
routine

sacrifice
satisfy
scheme
scholar
security
self-confidence
self-respect
separation
session
severe
simplify
solitary
specify
static
stray
suburbs
summarize
superior
surgery
survey
survival
suspicion

symbol
sympathy

temporary
tension
terminal
terrain
text
theme
thorough
threat
toll
toxic
tradition
tragedy
transparent
twilight

unexpectedly
unfavorable
unfortunate
unite
urge

vacuum
vault
vicinity
victim
victorious
villain
visual
vivid
vocal

wardrobe
widespread

yacht

NOTES

NOTES